National Curricula in Mathematics

Prepared for the Mathematical Association by

Geoffrey Howson

University of Southampton

The Mathematical Association

First published in 1991 by:
The Mathematical Association
259 London Road
Leicester LE2 3BE
England

ISBN 0 906 588 219 (paperback)

ISBN 0 906 588 243 (cased edition)

Produced at the University of Southampton.
Printed and bound in Great Britain at The Bath Press, Avon.

CONTENTS

INTRODUCTION AND ACKNOWLEDGEMENTS

It was suggested at a meeting of the Teaching Committee of the Mathematical Association, held at Sheffield in March, 1989, that a report giving details of educational systems in the European Community countries might prove valuable. At the time I declined an invitation to become involved, since "1992 and all that" caused me little concern compared with the likely effects of the national curriculum which had just been imposed in England and Wales. Later, I realised that one way of fighting what I saw as a misconceived scheme was to provide that information which would allow people to compare our practices, goals and expectations with those of others. (Here it should be emphasised that my objections were not directed against the principle of a national curriculum, but rather the manner in which it was being implemented in England and Wales.) Accordingly, I offered to produce this report. So as to increase its potential value, I have included descriptions of the national mathematics curricula of Hungary and Japan in addition to those of the EC countries.

Even though this report is quite extensive, there is much that it cannot describe. Little is said, for example, about teacher education and supply in the different countries. Although important matters, these lie outside the scope of the present book – perhaps they might form the theme of a future study. Certainly, there are great contrasts between, say, the shortage of mathematically qualified teachers in England, the deteriorating situation in France, and the position in Japan where there is great competition to become a mathematics teacher. Such differences clearly affect the ability of a system to 'deliver' a national curriculum. Neither is information given on how mathematics is actually taught in the various countries. Of course, this is extremely difficult to describe, for in any country there will be found a great variety of practices. Nevertheless, there are marked and significant differences to be observed. For example, in an impressive study of English mathematical education carried out immediately prior to the First World War, Georg Wolff (1915) remarked that in English classrooms there was more emphasis on 'written' work, and less on 'oral', than in their German counterparts. One suspects that this is still the case. Teaching methods and aims together form another crucial aspect of mathematics education within a country. Yet it is an aspect which cannot be adequately covered in this book. The present aim is more circumscribed: to look at the structure of systems and the curricular framework within which mathematics education takes place.

Some years ago, an American curriculum developer remarked to me that we in England led the world in giving individual lessons and in producing chapters of textbooks. Where he felt we failed was in putting these together to form a well-directed, coherent curriculum. It was an interesting accolade and criticism. Events since then have only served to make the criticism more telling. This report will not show "how it ought to be done", if indeed there is any royal road to curriculum construction. However, I hope it will alert readers both to possible pitfalls and also to possibilities that exist, will assist curriculum developers in many countries and, in particular, will lead to reconsideration of the present curriculum in England and Wales.

No book of this nature could have been prepared without enormous help from others. Mathematics educators in all the countries concerned have responded most generously to my requests for help. Official documents and data have been supplied in abundance; some provided translations, others checked my attempts to grapple with their language. Country descriptions have been passed backwards and forwards and have been gradually refined. No doubt some errors remain, but every attempt has been made to eradicate them.

Help, advice and criticism have been received from many friends and colleagues. Any attempt to list them would be bound to be blighted by omissions. I am most grateful to them all. Particular thanks are due, however, to the following:

Belgium: Gontran Ervynck, Guy Noël
Denmark: Bent Hirsberg
France: Bernard Cornu, Jean-Pierre Kahane, Jean-Philippe Labrousse
Germany: Ulrich Grevsmühl, Gert Schubring
Greece: Tasos Patronis, Despina Potari
Hungary: Tibor Nemetz, Julia Szendrei
Ireland: Elizabeth Oldham
Italy: Vinicio Villani
Japan: Eizo Nagasaki
Luxembourg: Lucien Kieffer
The Netherlands: Henk Schuring
Portugal: Paulo Abrantes, Elfrida Ramos de Matos Ralha
Spain: Claudi Alsina

I have also received much valuable advice and criticism from the panel which the Mathematical Association appointed to assist and guide me, Peter Coaker, John Hersee and Douglas Quadling.

The manuscript was typed by Mrs Margaret Youngs, Department of Mathematics, The University of Southampton, and by my family.

To all these I am most indebted. I hope that the book will prove sufficiently valuable to justify their combined help and encouragement.

Geoffrey Howson

December, 1990

Note

Whilst this report was in preparation, great changes took place in Germany. The system I describe is that of the former Federal Republic. However, it is the monolithic, centralised educational system of what was the Democratic Republic (East Germany) which will now have to adapt. The future educational system of Germany is likely to resemble that described in the report. Inevitably, though, data given on the number of Länder, the proportions of students in various types of school, etc, will soon become outdated.

PART 1

1

ASPECTS OF NATIONAL CURRICULA

1.1 National Curricula

It is well known that teachers throughout the world do not slavishly (or even unslavishly!) follow their national curriculum. What is 'intended' by those who draw up national curricula is never 'implemented' in all classrooms. (See, for example, Travers and Westbury (1989) and Robitaille and Garden (1989), for data on differences between intended and implemented mathematics curricula.) Moreover, what is learned by students may bear little relation to the implemented curriculum. Much that is taught is misunderstood, not understood or not retained. On the other hand, it is clear that students learn much mathematics away from the mathematics classroom, either in other lessons, in play, from brothers, sisters, parents etc., and from day–to–day activities. Are national curricula, therefore, so important? And if so, what is it about them which repays study?

In some ways, national curricula are like New Year resolutions – they are rarely 'kept' for long, but just as the resolutions tell us something about their makers, so a national curriculum carries a message about a system, its aims, aspirations and even what were perceived as shortcomings. In another sense, they resemble the Commandments. Few believers are successful in fully 'implementing' these – yet they act as markers and guides. Moreover, national curricula for mathematics reflect (or should do!) the way in which mathematics education is generally perceived in a country. To some they might appear to be randomly selected lists of topics taken from a mathematical lucky dip. But a national mathematical curriculum should have a clear educational, mathematical and pedagogical structure.

What does this last statement mean? First, institutionalised education must, for better or worse, serve certain national purposes. It must nurture and challenge those who are to provide a country with intellectual, technical, industrial and commercial leadership. There is, therefore, an élite for which the system must cater; and it is now accepted in most countries that entry to that élite must be open to all – it cannot be reserved for males, or those belonging to certain social classes or ethnic groups, or living in particular geographical areas. It is also increasingly important to provide a strong educational foundation for those 'of average ability'. These require an educational, and in particular a mathematical, foundation on which they can base technical and commercial studies both in senior high school years and in continuing education. Finally, there are those who may never aspire to such advanced understanding, but who, if they are to comprehend the world around them, and are to make a worthwhile contribution as democratic citizens and are not to be socially disadvantaged, will still need a grasp of basic mathematics. The ways in which countries attempt to meet these demands – indeed, how they interpret the problem (for example, the definition which they give to the word 'basic') – differ greatly. It is, of course, an issue much connected with that of differentiation of curricula.

1.2 National Curricula in Mathematics

What of mathematics? The subject can be viewed in many ways: for example, as a collection of interesting and potentially useful results, methods and techniques; as an abstract structure with seemingly miraculous inter–relationships – for example, the relationship $e^{\pi i} = -1$, or that the probability of two randomly chosen naturals being co–prime is $6/\pi^2$; or as an activity that relies upon the participant's ability to conjecture, prove, generalize, model, apply, define, ... How are these aspects of mathematics displayed within, and encouraged by, the curriculum? How do the emphases placed on different aspects differ? Does the curriculum offer a consistent, accurate, and representative view of mathematics and mathematical activity?

Finally, a national mathematics curriculum cannot be simply a list of mathematical topics. It must also be concerned with the learning of mathematics. One hardly expects to see a national curriculum built upon a specific theory of learning, but the need must be acknowledged to provide time for material to be understood, conflicts to be recognised and resolved, techniques to be acquired, knowledge to be assimilated and revised, and mental structures to be developed. A national curriculum should not set mathematical goals which are hopelessly at odds with what we know about the cognitive development of children, and the time allotted to the teaching of mathematics must be commensurate with the demands made.

1.3 Teachers and Change

Yet the curriculum in any subject is not constrained only by the pupils' cognitive development. It is important that the constraints imposed by teachers are not overlooked. A curriculum which is not understood by teachers will quickly fail – and there are numerous examples from the 1960s and 1970s to remind us of that. Of course, one cannot always select a curriculum from the common knowledge of the teaching force, but the enormous difficulty and expense of effective, rather than merely notional, in–service training must be recognised. Moreover, teachers' knowledge is only one constraint: teachers' time is another. The teacher's week is bounded and there is much to fit into it if teaching is to be effective: the preparation and delivery of lessons, the marking of homework and tests and, of great importance, professional advancement, eg reading, attending meetings, learning and seeing how others teach, and becoming acquainted with new technology. A national curriculum which imposes major administrative burdens on the teacher cuts substantially into the teacher's week. Something will have to go and it is essential to ask whether the gains will outweigh the losses.

Technology now imposes major constraints. It is interesting to note which countries assume that every pupil will have ready access to a calculator, or that micros are sufficiently abundant in schools to permit their use being built into the curriculum. Again, one must ask to what extent those assumptions on the existence of hardware are justified and, if they are not, whether money will be made available to remedy this.

The fact that technology changes rapidly draws attention to another major problem. It is one thing to have a national curriculum, another to have one which permits development: to adapt the old Latin tag of Publilius Syrus, 'Malum est curriculum quod mutari non potest' – it's a bad curriculum which cannot be changed! Curriculum development has not proved easy to effect in many countries. In some cases change is inhibited by the structure within which the curriculum is defined. Designing that initial structure with eventual change in mind is essential. Regrettably, it is rarely done.

What, however, is the role of the teacher to be within a national curriculum? To what degree should a national curriculum guide and to what extent should it prescribe and circumscribe? The answers to these last questions differ very markedly from country to country. In some, teaching sequences are given in some detail, hours to be spent on individual topics may be suggested, the choice of textbooks limited. In others, only brief aims and requirements for certain key stages are given and the teacher and examiner are given considerable freedom to interpret.

Often a 'curriculum' is thought of as comprising various components: aims and objectives, content, teaching methods, evaluation and assessment. The national curricula outlined vary greatly on what they say on teaching methods – a most vital component. Frequently, too, they leave the assessment of the pupils in the hands of the teacher. This is seen and accepted as part of a teacher's job and, clearly, if a student's promotion to the next class or to the next stage of education depends upon the teacher's assessment, then this is a responsibility not to be undertaken lightly.

When considering a national curriculum, the responsibility and autonomy granted to the teacher must always be considered, bearing in mind that responsibilities can only be assigned when teachers are prepared (in both senses) to accept them.

What is the role of teachers in preparing a national curriculum? Here again practice differs considerably, ranging from almost total lack of input, through meaningless consultation, to long term discussions between widely representative groups including teacher associations and subject specialists.

It has been pointed out that the effectiveness of a doctor's injection is not dependent upon his or her belief in its power, whereas a teacher must believe in the effectiveness and value of what he or she is doing if it is to be truly successful. Teachers will have no great commitment to making an imposed curriculum succeed. Yet, frequently, curriculum development projects succeed, particularly in their initial stages, because the teachers participating feel intimately involved.

Sound educational structures can help to provide motivation for all types of pupils; well-planned national curricula can set clear targets and criteria and can bring homogeneity in their wake. Well-structured, well-written and well-presented material can enhance teaching and, to some extent, compensate where good teachers are absent. But essentially good teaching depends upon good teachers, and they must be given a considerable degree of autonomy. A national curriculum which ignores this will secure homogeneity at the expense of quality.

2

NATIONAL CURRICULA: POINTS OF DIVERGENCE

In the last chapter we briefly considered various features of a national curriculum and also factors likely to affect it. We shall now look again at them in some detail, drawing upon the outlines of curricula and syllabuses printed in Part 2 of this book.

The restriction to EC countries plus Hungary and Japan, is a very severe one. These countries have a certain cultural communality which is not shared by, for example, China or Tanzania. Many of the remarks made will, accordingly, have limited validity, and this fact must be borne in mind by the reader. It should also be pointed out that, with one notable exception, data are not presented in tabular form so as to provide "easy" comparisons. There is no "easy" way of comparing what is done and what is achieved in various countries. Major differences in philosophy and structure make simplistic comparisons dangerous. Our aim is to encourage readers to examine how curricula and expectations vary from country to country, but the only way to do this in a serious manner is to read through each country's national curriculum with care. Even then, it must be remembered that the accounts given are only summaries of what, in many cases, are very extensive documents.

2.1 National Systems

Each national description is prefaced by a diagram illustrating the country's educational system and it is these which demonstrate the first points of divergence. National school systems reflect social cultures and traditions, and are much influenced by economic considerations, past and present. Perhaps the simplest measure of the latter is the length of compulsory schooling. This can be as high as 12 years, but Portugal, for example, is only just moving away from a 6–year system. However, even this must be interpreted with care. In England, schooling is compulsory until the age of 16, in Japan until 15. Yet, over 90 per cent of Japanese students remain in school after 15. So, taking into account the high truancy rates for inner–city schools in England, it is likely that on any one day there are proportionately more 15 year–olds at school in Japan than in England where attendance is "compulsory".

Problems arise also at the beginning of compulsory education. In many countries almost all children attend some type of pre–primary institution well before they reach the age of compulsory attendance. Sometimes, as in France, the pre-primary schools are integrated into the state educational system and have trained teachers and an embryonic curriculum. On the other hand, in Germany pre-school education, although widespread, is deliberately kept informal and separate from the school system proper even though most of it is state funded. The existence, or otherwise, of readily available pre-primary education and the forms which it takes will almost certainly have a marked influence on children's attainment, expectations and behaviour in the early years of compulsory primary education.

Not all the countries in the survey have yet moved to universal secondary education. This, combined with other national differences relating to the beginning of compulsory education and, in the case of Germany and England, regional differences in the age of transfer from primary to secondary education, means that the duration of primary/elementary education and the grades it spans differ considerably. (Note that to facilitate comparisons we have adopted a common "grade" system when describing curricula.)

It is at secondary level, however, that differences in the structures of the various systems become most pronounced. This reflects not only different assumptions as to the desirability of streaming children by ability and attainment, but also different beliefs and traditions considering the degree to which the student's curriculum should be tailored to ability, aptitude and aspirations. That children differ greatly in the rate at which they progress is not a new discovery and all countries make some allowance for this. However, they do so in very different ways. It is important when considering a national educational system, therefore, to ask such questions as:

> What means are used to cater for individual differences ?
>
> Are there separate clearly-defined goals for different groups of students ?
>
> How are students assigned to different streams ?
>
> Does the overall curriculum differ between streams ?
>
> In what way does the mathematics curriculum differ between streams, what assumptions underlie any differences, and exactly how are the differences manifested ?
>
> What possibilities exist for switching streams ?
>
> Is automatic annual promotion assumed or do some pupils repeat years ?

Is there differentiation even within streams ?

Which streams lead on to higher education and which to further (technical and vocational) education ?

So far as actual structures are concerned, four ways of dealing with the problems of differentiation can be identified in the national descriptions supplied below.

(i) No differentiation of students and curricula other than at the teacher's discretion (e.g. Denmark, Japan (in both cases until Grade 9)).

(ii) Differentiation through the provision of 'optional material' within the main course (e.g. Belgium, Germany (where this is provided within differentiated streams)), or through the provision of 'extra' mathematics (e.g. Belgium and (in Grade 9) Japan).

(iii) Differentiation through clearly separate school types, or streams within a single school (e.g. Germany, the Netherlands).

(iv) Differentiation by individual rate of progress through a common curriculum (e.g. England, but note that here in some subjects other than mathematics (ii) appears to be the preferred alternative).

Each of these four approaches sets peculiar challenges to the teacher, to the curriculum designer, and to the student.

National policies on streaming, on comprehensive v. bipartite or tripartite education etc, generally affect the curriculum as a whole and mathematics only as a special case. However, it is a feature of national curricula (at least, since the post-revolutionary USSR elementary school curriculum, based on the three themes 'nature, work and society', was rejected) that they are expressed in terms of subject disciplines and of content within disciplines. Clearly, the way in which mathematics is differentiated will have implications for the teaching of other subjects which use it and, again, this is a factor which must be borne in mind when considering the benefits and drawbacks of different systems.

The four types of differentiation which have been mentioned do not necessarily apply at all stages of education. Most countries are unwilling explicitly to differentiate curricula in the early primary years. Of course, teachers are expected to respond to the different needs of individual children, but, outside the United Kingdom, differences in expectation are not specifically built into national curricula. On the other hand, in most countries, a range of curricula, both general and mathematical, is available for students beyond the age of 14. Education at that level is often provided in a tripartite form with academic, technical and vocational streams, each with its own goals and leaving qualifications. In the Netherlands and Germany such divisions begin about age 11 (although in a form which, for a year or two, facilitates transfers), in Luxembourg and France later. Indeed, a feature of the two last–named countries is the very rich and varied range of mathematical syllabuses offered by schools in response to differing academic and vocational needs.

In the years of post–compulsory schooling it is usual for a number of curricular alternatives to be offered (possibly including that of not taking mathematics). At this level the school curriculum can take many forms. (For this reason we have had to be much more selective in the second section of this book when describing mathematics curricula in the secondary high schools, ie, the years of post–compulsory education.) We note here, for example, the broad, but very differently designed, curricula to be found in the Netherlands and France contrasted with the narrow, specialised study traditionally favoured in England. At this level the time devoted to mathematics by different groups of students begins to vary significantly.

Lower down the secondary school about four 50 minute periods a week would seem the norm, although there is still some variation – Italy, for example, having a smaller time allocation and the keen young mathematician in Belgium a far greater one (6 periods). Here it is perhaps worth noting that a widening of the main school curriculum and, on occasion, a reduction in the number of school hours has meant that in a number of countries the time allocation for mathematics in the lower secondary school has recently been reduced (eg Denmark, England and Hungary).

It is important, then, to see how a country caters for different abilities, attainments, aptitudes and ambitions. However, even if there are clearly defined streams, the models used for the differentiation of content and teaching may still differ.

Between 1985 and 1989, the model used in England for main–school secondary students was that of "nesting". National criteria for 16 year–olds were prescribed at three levels, for high–, average– and low–attainers, and these were "nested" in the manner of Russian dolls. In Ireland, for example, an apparently similar scheme is used, but now we note more clearly defined differences in expected content and in methods of treatment (see, eg, the syllabuses for geometry and bear in mind that, for example, those following Syllabuses A and B are likely to proceed to different types of Leaving Certificate course). The model of differentiation defined in the new, English "Programmes of Study" is a more basic form of nesting. It is the "piece of spaghetti" model – one swallows as much as one can in the time available.

Other models can be found elsewhere. An obvious difference between the three types of school in Baden–Württemberg is the amount of stress placed on commercial arithmetic. More interestingly, mensuration formulae are introduced in the Hauptschule earlier than in the Gymnasium. This is probably justified on the grounds that mensuration is an important goal for both types of pupil, but that low-attainers will need more time to grasp the material; hence, begin earlier and pace the work more slowly. This argument contrasts markedly with the assumptions on teaching and learning implicit in other national curricula.

Note should be taken, then, of the extent to which differentiated curricula stipulate different content inputs and express differing expectations concerning outputs (eg, no proofs of geometrical theorems examined at Level B in Ireland, none given at Level C).

Two approaches to differentiation in the upper secondary school merit special attention. One is in the Netherlands. There students, within the same differentiated stream, are offered a choice of syllabuses. The first, A, stresses the use of mathematics in modelling, particularly in social and economic contexts, and its content includes discrete mathematics (including matrices), probability and statistics. The second, B, treats analysis (calculus) and geometry in a more traditional manner. The two syllabuses are intended to cater for different needs and do so in a way which allows students not only to opt for either, but in the case of the pre-university stream, for both.

The other is in Japan, where an attempt has been made to distinguish between syllabuses which primarily aim to provide "mathematical literacy" and those designed to inculcate "mathematical thought". Fuller explanations of these terms are to be found in Howson and Wilson (1986). It is an interesting dichotomy which has parallels at the undergraduate level between, respectively, "service" and "mathematics major" courses. What is not so clear is where in this dichotomy the computer fits. In Japan, it appears in the "thought" part of the curriculum and, given the suggested treatment, there are good reasons for this. However, at a university level, the intelligent use of software would seem an essential part of a "literacy" course. Does this indicate a significant divide between school and university mathematics, or is it the case that the Japanese conception is over–conservative? This is a problem to which all curriculum developers must respond in the next decade.

These, then, are certain points of divergence arising, in particular, from different philosophies on streaming students according to aptitude and "likely" (with a great deal of self–fulfilling prophecy) career and employment.

Another important feature of educational systems is the size and influence of the independent (ie, non state–funded) sector. The size varies greatly from country to country and is not always directly related to social and educational influence. Independent schools can be marked more for their religious affiliations than for any other reason. At the upper–secondary level in Japan, though, independent schools are both numerous and highly influential. However, they are still bound by the national curriculum. This is true in most countries, but not in England and Wales. Even here, though, the links between the external examination system and the national curriculum restrict the freedom of the influential independent schools. In these countries, as in several others (eg, Denmark and Hungary) the proportion of children attending independent schools has risen in recent years.

Students receiving state education may also receive additional, parentally–funded tuition out of school. The extent of this varies widely both between and within countries. It is, however, a significant feature of Japanese and Greek education. As the commentary on Japan suggests, its provision there would appear to help support the non–differentiated school curriculum, by both stretching the higher attainer and helping the weaker pupil.

2.2 Presenting a curriculum

The most immediate and striking point of divergence between the various national curricula is effectively concealed from the readers of this book , namely their physical size. There is an enormous range between the expansive Spanish documents and those of, say, Denmark.

In the case of Spain and Portugal, the need for comprehensive documentation is apparent. School systems are being expanded considerably and new educational opportunities are being created. There is a need to spell out intentions in great detail to those teachers who will be taking the new courses. Elsewhere, the amount of detail often seems related to the faith which the national authorities are prepared to place in their teaching forces.

What would seem essential, but is often ignored, is the need to provide curricula with in–built flexibility. Over–prescriptive curricula set into over–elaborate frameworks will prove very difficult to amend: they will not permit and encourage gradual evolution and improvement. It is possible to build regular revision of curricula into the educational system, as is the case in Japan where syllabuses are reviewed every ten years or so – but who can say, bearing in mind the current rates of technological advance, that the recently revised, and still to be implemented,

Japanese syllabuses will continue to make sense in the opening years of the 21st century?

If a syllabus is not statutory, ie, not legally binding, as in Germany, as opposed to statutory, as in England, then its inappropriateness matters little. The Realschule syllabus in North Rhine Westphalia is a case in point. There, a group of teachers, teacher–trainers and administrators is currently working on syllabus revision, but there is no great hurry, for the curriculum within the schools has already evolved from that set out in the official documents. The new curriculum, when it eventually emerges, will be there to guide rather than to constrain.

What can happen when the framework is too tightly prescribed (and the legislative procedures arthritic) can be seen at its worst in the general school curriculum for Italy. There, the timetabled hours for the secondary high schools have not been changed since the 1920s and aspiring mathematicians have still to devote more hours a week to Latin than to mathematics. At least, they will have no difficulty in appreciating the previously–quoted Latin maxim in the original language. (There have, however, been significant changes in subject curricula in recent years.)

There is a widespread belief (for which supporting evidence appears to be non–existent) that teachers' practices can be significantly changed by means of legislation: in particular, by the provision of detailed curricula to be followed. Readers of this book will not be able to judge exactly in what detail the various curricula are set out. Nevertheless, they can consider the freedom given to teachers to omit, insert or re–order material and to adjust emphases whilst still observing statutory requirements. (Is, for example, content prescribed to be taught within a given grade, eg, Greece, or within a certain "key stage", eg, Italy and Spain.?) It is this freedom that can help bring individuality and life to mathematics teaching, and can actively enhance the processes of curriculum development.

The provision of time for teacher– or pupil–chosen options can also encourage experimentation. Here, of course, assessment procedures can prove an inhibiting factor and we shall consider these in more detail in Section 2.9.

We have commented earlier on the way in which national curricula must, almost of necessity, concentrate on "content" and be thought of almost entirely in "content" terms. The dangers of this are widely recognised and a variety of means have been employed to overcome them. In Spain, for example, alongside lists of "facts, concepts and principles", "procedures" and "algorithms and competencies", there are also lists of "general strategies" and, under the heading of "attitudes, values and norms", statements referring to aspects of mathematical appreciation and to organisational and work habits. Again, the primary school curriculum for Ireland is, in reality, an attractively produced teachers' guide. England and Wales attempt to build process goals, in particular, ones relating to using and applying mathematics, into the framework which they have adopted. In this book we can only hint at the numerous ways in which national curricula have sought to influence teaching methods in addition to content: attempts which, as was stated earlier, can encourage and supplement other endeavours, but which by themselves appear to have achieved little.

2.3 Aims

The aims of national curricula can be overt or hidden. The latter, which reflect political opinions and strivings, and social and cultural traditions and assumptions, are in many ways the more interesting. Yet, because of their nature, interpretation is very much a subjective activity. Let us, as an example, briefly consider an interpretation given twenty years ago. Speaking at ICME 2 (Exeter, 1972), René Thom claimed that the modern mathematics movement concealed, but was in part driven by, "a feeling of frustration in the mathematics community ... : jealousy with regard to Physicists, favoured financially by the development of nuclear energy ...; jealousy with regard to Biologists, made famous by the discovery of DNA and the genetic code. During these same years ... great advances [in mathematics] ... did not arouse the interest of the general public. ... It was in order to revive this declining interest that recourse was made to 'modern mathematics'" (Thom, 1973). This is clearly a serious, subjective view concerning unstated aims underpinning 1960s' curricula. Other, similar inferences, valid or not, can be drawn from those of today; implications, for example, concerning views on class structures and on the wishes of governments to reinforce or remove them. This book, however, would not seem an appropriate place for such speculation. Yet the reader must be warned that the aims of curricula are not merely those to be found at the front of official documents. The mere existence of a national curriculum creates power for some group or other and brings in its wake a switch in the balance of power, authority and influence. It would be naive not to realise the political implications of a national curriculum even in mathematics.

A curriculum also means power at a subject level: Thom's views might well be interpreted, rightly or wrongly, as arising from the fact that at that time power and influence within mathematics education in France had been grasped by others. Not only did this mean that control was in other hands, but a philosophy of mathematics which Thom opposed was now being propagated – indeed, statutorily enforced. Here we move onto safer, if still contentious, ground. Unstated philosophies of mathematics are more readily and accurately identified – at least by mathematics educators. Some commentators might well use the umbrella title of "modern mathematics" for all the developments of the 1960s and 1970s. However, there were considerable differences between the aims of, and courses devised by, say, SMP (UK), SMSG (USA), and those responsible for curriculum development in France, Japan and the USSR.

Oddly enough, such differences are not so readily apparent in the curricula which we summarise below. The influences of the 1960s linger on in some countries more than others, as, indeed, do those of the 1900s. What we cannot find are new curricula driven almost in their entirety by particular themes or ideologies, whether these concern technology and the computer, or particular theories of learning. There is no one view of mathematics having an influence comparable with that of Bourbaki, and none of learning similar to that of Bruner and Dienes. Instead, there are amalgams, largely distinguished from each other by variations in emphasis. Utility, in a very limited sense, would now seem to be given more emphasis, even in the academic streams, and rigour less. The content "inflation" of the 1960s and 1970s has been followed in many countries by a slimming of syllabuses. Here, another hidden influence must be recognised. The last two decades have seen a great increase in the numbers of students taking advanced mathematics courses and there have been pressures everywhere to make these more "accessible". How to do this without detracting from the opportunities provided for those who could cope with, and rejoice in, the older, more technically demanding, syllabuses, has proved a major (and largely unanswered) question in all countries. A baccalauréat for almost all is, for example, an important social and political aim. However, if this carries with it open entry to university, then there are considerable 'knock-on' effects, as is now becoming evident in France. Similarly, in the German Gymnasiums of some Länder, curricula which were constructed for an élite of 10% or so, are now available, on parental demand, to a very much greater proportion of the cohort.

Let us, however, briefly turn to some of the overt aims to be found in national curricula. The claims of Northern Ireland that we teach mathematics because:

> "of its use in everyday life,
> it can be enjoyable,
> of its value as a subject in its own right,
> of its application to other subjects"

are uncontroversially typical.

Elsewhere we find more interesting aims (and claims). In the Italian syllabus we find that one aim is to help students use normal language precisely. The French look to mathematics:

> developing reasoning powers: observation, analysis, deductive thought;
> stimulating the imagination;
> promoting the habit of clear expression, both written and oral;
> stressing the qualities of proceeding methodically and with care.

Utility, then, need not necessarily be interpreted in a narrow manner.

2.4 Calculators and Micros

In most countries of which we write, calculators are now built into the curriculum. However, there are still those in which references to their use are marginal. For example, the Irish lower secondary school curriculum, implemented in the late 1980s, still contains items such as "use of square root and square tables". Often, too, we note that calculator use does not appear to be prescribed, or actively encouraged, in the primary school. Even in the secondary school, the use of more advanced types of calculators is rarely mentioned. France calls for the use of programmable calculators in the highest grades, but there are no specific references to the use of calculators with graphic capabilities (although Spain gives a blanket welcome to all types of calculating and computing devices, and their use is, in a sense, officially supported in England). It is interesting that Japan still expects teachers to introduce pupils to the use of the soroban, the Japanese–style abacus. This possesses pedagogical advantages over the electronic calculator in certain circumstances. Perhaps the most interesting curriculum, so far as the absorption of the calculator is concerned, is that for England and Wales. Here there has been considerable experimentation, particularly in the primary schools. Moreover, the views of influential politicians who still place great weight on the need for all to be able to carry out the algorithms for long multiplication and long division had to be heeded. As a result, it is clearly set out what is expected with or without the use of a calculator.

The position with respect to micros is more varied. There is little evidence of their existence having significantly affected the content of mathematics syllabuses. Usually, it is expected that they will be used to illuminate and enrich the teaching of traditional material. In several countries micro work is expected of all students following a particular course. Not surprisingly, these courses are usually at secondary level. Thus, in Denmark all senior pupils specializing in mathematics are expected to spend about 20 hours on a topic such as fractals, Computer Assisted Design, or linear programming. Elsewhere, eg Japan, algorithmics and programming are included in certain options.

Further down the school, with the exception of the United Kingdom, the micro, when mentioned, is expected to be used as a general aid to teaching and learning wherever appropriate, but its use is not prescribed in particular contexts. Only in the United Kingdom is its use for certain purposes statutorily prescribed. Some of these uses, eg that of statistical packages to assist data analysis, would seem unexceptionable. Others appear more problematic.

2.5 The core curriculum

It has often been argued that there is a core of "key content" to be found in the curricula of schools throughout the world. Not surprisingly, therefore, since the countries we describe come from a fairly narrow, economic band and share many traditions of schooling, there is considerable agreement about what a school curriculum should contain. Differences arise in the age at which content is introduced (and what is difficult to tell from national curricula is the degree of formality with which topics are first encountered and the expected outcomes so far as pupils are concerned) and in the percentage of the age cohort who will be exposed to particular topics and expected to achieve (an undisclosed degree of) mastery over them.

Later in this section we list this key content together with ages of introduction in certain specimen countries. The reader is warned again of all the difficulties associated with the construction and interpretation of such comparative tables! This table was drawn up by Eizo Nagasaki of the National Institute for Educational Research, Tokyo to whom I am much indebted.

It will be seen that there are occasional gaps, where interpretation has proved difficult, and that in the cases of France and Italy key stages for the introduction of a topic are given rather than a particular grade. The data for West Germany refer to the Land of Baden-Württemberg. Under the column headed H is the appropriate year for pupils in the Hauptschule (the "lowest" of the three streams), under G those for the Gymnasium (grammar school). The UK "levels" are difficult to interpret (they have different meanings in England and Northern Ireland - see the "content" table below and the national survey): the following table gives the author's interpretation based on the graph reprinted in the national survey.

Level	Year *attained* by median pupil	Percentage expected to attain by 16
2	7	100
3	9	96
4	11	90
5	13	78
6	15	60
7		40
8		22
9		10
10		4

(It would appear that the statutory English "programmes of study" assume that students will not proceed to study the topics at any level until they have attained the previous level. However, non–statutory, yet official, guidance advises against this course of action, and suggests that teachers work within key stages. The Northern Ireland programmes of study are set out differently. Thus, all secondary school pupils there will meet the formula for the area of a triangle. However, it is still assumed that only a quarter or so of students will attain mastery of it, ie its "level" has not been reduced. A * in the table indicates that the item appears in a different, but adjacent, level in Northern Ireland; ** indicates two levels away.)

It will be seen that the table (and – if the reader cares to draw one up – a corresponding table for all the countries described in this book) contains many interesting features. For some topics there is comparatively little "spread" in the age of introduction, eg decimals. In others the spread can be six or eight years, eg prime numbers and the introduction of numerical probabilities. In general, though, there is a not unexpected degree of agreement to be found amongst items traditionally to be found in syllabuses.

Even within this key content there are still, in certain problematic areas, different approaches to be found. In 1912, in a comparative study for the forerunner of ICMI, Fujiwara, the Japanese correspondent, wrote:

"In former days when we blindly followed some of the English and American textbooks ... it was customary to teach fractions first and then decimals considered as special types of fractions. [Now, ie 1912,] decimals are introduced as soon as possible as an extension of the denary system of notation ... decimals are taken up very early and fractions put off till very late and not much importance is attached to them."

COUNTRY	Belgium (Flanders)	France	Germany (B–W)		Italy	Japan	England
CONTENT			H	G			
Arithmetic							
Decimals	9	9–11	11	11	8–11	8	L3
Negative numbers	8	11–12	12	12	11–14	12	L3
Operations on these	12	12–13	12	12	11–14	12	L5
Fractions	7	9–11	11	11	8–11	8	L4
Operations on these	8	11–12	11	11	11–14	8	L8
Percentages	9	11–12	12	12	11–14	10	L4
Proportion	13	9–11	12	12	11–14	11	L5*
Primes	8		11	11	8–11	14	L5
Square roots	12	14–15	14	14	11–14	14	L5
Hcf	8		11	11	11–14	10	L7
Scientific notation	13	13–14	14	15		13	L8
Algebra							
Set notation	12		11	11	8–11	15	–
Use of letters	12–13	11–12		12	11–14	10	L5
Linear equations	12	12–13	12	12	11–14	12	L6
Quadratics	15	14–15	–	14	14–16	14	L6*
Linear graphs	14	14–15		13	14–16	13	L7*
Transposing formulae				15	11–14	13	L8
Factorising	13	14–15		14		14	L10
Geometry							
Symmetry	8	7–9		6	8–11	11	L3
Congruence	9		12	13	11–14	10	L5
2D reprn of 3D	16	7–9	13			9	L6
Pythagoras	14	13–14	14	14	11–14	14	L7
Area formulae	10	9–11	13	14	11–14	10	L8
Volume formulae	11	14–15	14	14		11	L8
Trigonometry of right triangle	14	14–15	–	15	14–16	15	L8
Scaling of dimensions		14–15			11–14	14	L9*
SSS,SAS,etc	13			13		12	L9
Vectors	9	14–15				16	L8*
Statistics and Probability							
Means (averages)	10	14–15	14		8–11	10	L4**
Simple numerical probability	11	14–15		10	11–14	14	L4
Pie charts		11–12	12		11–14	10	L5
Independent events		17–18		17–19	14–16	15	L8
New Technology							
Flow charts					8–11	16	L7
Calculator use	14	11	14		8–11	10	L3
Micro use	15–16	11			14–16	12	L4*

Table 1: Age of introduction of content

Questions relating to the introduction of decimals and fractions still appear to cause problems. Moreover, now that greater proportions of pupils stay on at school and have to grapple with algebra and algebraic expressions, the value of work on arithmetical fractions has had to be reconsidered.

2.6 Other curricular considerations

As was mentioned in Section 2.3, there would now seem to be less emphasis on abstract, structural approaches to curriculum building. Work on sets appears in the curricula of most countries, but there is now less emphasis on building up ideas of number through cardinality (at the expense of ordinality), on equivalence relations, and on the extension of number systems through ordered pairs and the use of equivalence classes. Representation of numbers in different number bases is still included in the curricula of many countries.

At a higher level, complex numbers have always been on the fringe of school syllabuses. It is, then, interesting to see them included in one French course "essentially for cultural reasons". Mathematics as a cultural activity and component is given scant recognition in most countries. The inclusion of "philosophical questions of mathematics" in the Hungarian high school curriculum, therefore, merits special attention.

The general area of school algebra pre–16 shows relatively few variations. In some countries, informal, and on occasion algorithmic, numerical methods for the solution of equations are now being given more emphasis, and there is greater acceptance of graphical methods of solution. The amount of emphasis given to algebraic manipulation is a point of divergence.

Work on algebraic structures, such as groups, is now to be found only in the upper grades of a few systems, sometimes as an option.

Although there is considerable agreement on how to teach algebra, comparative studies suggest that the task is not very successfully accomplished. There is still a marked need to improve our teaching. For this reason the new French lower secondary school curriculum holds especial interest. On paper, and in its unabridged form, it seems a particularly well–designed approach. It will be interesting to see how it succeeds in the classroom.

The agreement to be observed in the teaching of algebra does not carry over into geometry, at least beyond those years of primary school which are usually devoted to an exploration of location, shape, size and space. Here there are indications of many exciting opportunities for the enthusiastic, knowledgeable teacher, such as "solids in technology, art and nature" (Portugal, Grade 5). (That country's "use of the plumb line and spirit level" at Grade 4 also provides a valuable link between the building site and the classroom, the concrete (not intended!) and the abstract.)

Later work on geometry varies very much from country to country. Certainly, there is much common work on transformations, but important differences in the design of courses can be found. Traditional Euclid has almost disappeared. Fittingly, he is still to be found in the upper grades in Greece (where the course is particularly abstract and structurally oriented). Elsewhere, "neighbourhoods" of Euclid remain, for example, consequences of the congruence conditions for the triangle, and the circle theorems. Big differences arise from the extent to which geometry explicitly (or implicitly) seeks to emphasise (or display) deductive thought and structure. Here, again, the French lower secondary school syllabus is of interest in exhibiting directed mathematical thought. This is, of course, no guarantee that the underlying structure will be perceived by either the teacher giving, or the student following, the course.

Again, traditional work on ruler, compasses and set square constructions are given very different degrees of emphasis, as also are such practical concerns as how to represent, and to interpret representations of, 3-D objects in 2-D, map reading and the earth as a sphere.

Traditions in geometry teaching, nineteenth century influences on school systems and current attitudes to proof can all be assessed, in a rough and ready way, by the references which syllabuses make to Thales' Theorem (or its equivalents). First, if the theorem concerns a circle (that the diameter subtends a right angle on the circumference), we are in a country influenced by Germany (eg Austria, Hungary). However, if the theorem concerns the ratio of corresponding lengths in a similarity (eg what in England was known as the mid-point theorem or in German-speaking countries the Strahlensatz), then this displays a French influence. (The reader may draw his or her own inference if there is no mention of Thales.) More importantly, the presence of the theorem can reveal not only an attempt to demonstrate proof in mathematics, but even if no proof is provided, an attempt to show that one aim of the mathematician is to identify significant results and give them a special status (at one time, as something to be remembered; nowadays, perhaps, as a result worth recording which can be used as the basis for further arguments or deductions).

The whole difficult problem of "proof" is approached in a variety of ways. In some respects, "proof" is ill–suited to appearances in national curricula. It is a concept, and a technique, that must be acquired over a long period through examples and practice. Understanding and techniques must gradually be extended and deepened. The reader, then, is asked to pay particular attention to the way in which the various curricula reprinted below provide opportunities for, and encourage the development of, logical argument and deductive proof. What, for example, is said about the introduction and understanding of logical connectives, of logical equivalence, of implication, and of converse statements?

Probability and statistics have effectively entered the school curriculum within the last fifty years. As a result, their treatment differs very much from country to country. There is a marked difference between, say, the applications–oriented approach to probability to be found in English senior high schools, and the references in the Baden–Württemberg curriculum to Kolmogorov and von Mises. Descriptive statistics is now almost universally regarded as part of "mathematics for all" and, as the table indicates, there is relatively little variation in the age at which such topics as pie charts are introduced. Where significant differences occur is in the treatment of more advanced statistics, eg random variables, sampling, regression and correlation, and of probability. The more recent the syllabus, the more ambitious is the treatment of probability likely to be. A corollary to this statement is that the more ambitious syllabuses are at the moment "hopes" rather than "proven successes". Their progress will be watched with interest (but note the discouraging messages to be found in the national summary for Hungary). Certainly, the development of worthwhile and successful probability courses for all will prove a major challenge in the next decade.

In the curricula of some countries, probability is linked with combinatorics. Certainly, some approaches to teaching probability associate the topic very much with combinations and permutations. This, however, can lead to a restricted view of the subject. In Spain, graphs and statistics are paired together. One suspects that this linking could also prove somewhat detrimental to the former. Nevertheless, combinatorics is now deservedly being given more attention: perhaps because it is seen as part of that currently fashionable, if ill–defined, area, discrete mathematics. Curiously, though, particularly in view of its popularity in the 1960s, the useful inclusion and exclusion formula is rarely explicitly mentioned in national curricula. What appears to be a largely unresearched and unanswered problem concerns the age at which combinatorial ideas are best introduced and developed.

Elementary graph theory is now taught in the upper secondary school, often as an option, for example, in England, Hungary and the Netherlands. However, in

England the "use of networks to solve problems" is now expected of bright primary school pupils, and of low-attaining 15 year-olds. The example given is to "find the shortest route for a person delivering the post". One can only infer that the network must be taken to be small and that a rough-and-ready, trial and improvement solution is sought. The primary school would hardly seem the place for the teaching and/or developing of general algorithms and heuristic methods. Matrices have yet to establish a firm hold within the school curriculum. Interesting applications of their use are to be found within the upper secondary "A" syllabuses in the Netherlands.

Applications are paid considerable lip-service. In some instances this can mean much emphasis on commercial arithmetic or technicians' geometry and mensuration, especially in the "lower" streams. Elsewhere, as in the Netherlands, it can represent genuine attempts to mine the rich variety of mathematical models to be found in biology, economics, etc. England still preserves its long tradition of teaching Newtonian Mechanics within the upper secondary mathematics classroom. It is, however, a tradition under threat, as most students no longer also study physics as they did in the past, and the alternative claims of statistics for a place in the curriculum are now more widely advanced.

The use of project work is a valuable way of showing (and learning) how mathematics is applied. It is becoming well-established in England and one notes that the optional Grade 9 course in Japan also asks for the use of "field or laboratory work, experiment and investigation".

2.7 Learning

Any national curriculum carries with it assumptions concerning both what it is felt desirable for students to know, and also what it is possible for them to learn and how they might best learn it.

Assumptions concerning what is within a student's cognitive grasp tend to draw our immediate attention - particularly if we are able to recall some of the eccentricities of the 1960s. Eyebrows, then, are raised when, for example, one sees Lagrange's Theorem for groups in the North Rhine Westphalia Realschule syllabus for "average" 15 year-olds, or "distinguishing between estimates of probabilities based on statistical evidence and those based on the assumptions of symmetry" in that for English primary schools. In a sense these can be seen as matters of experiment, but it can be argued that a national curriculum should be drawn from successfully piloted content and approaches rather than be part pipe dream.

Less immediately obvious are the assumptions concerning how students learn. Elucidation can often be obtained from non–statutory guidance and other teachers' material. First, however, one must ask what exactly it is that a national curriculum is setting out to describe. Is it meant to indicate what should take place in classrooms, the type of activities in which students are expected to engage, or is it describing what students should know at the end of the grade, key stage or course?

Here the French lower secondary school curriculum is helpful in distinguishing between:

> prescribed activities which should be as rich and diverse as possible,
> expected knowledge which will be much less than the mathematics touched upon in class, and
> possible complementary activities.

That the "implemented" curriculum must, of necessity, go beyond the envisaged "attained" is recognised by many countries. Again, as an example, Japan stresses that if children are to understand two digit numbers, which is their goal for attainment, then they should be introduced to three digit ones. A "programme of study", *pace* the English, cannot consist solely of what it is hoped to attain.

The idea that understanding will be developed gradually and at increasingly more complex cognitive levels is most clearly embodied in the primary school curriculum for Dutch–speaking Belgium. Here the same topic is included in the syllabuses for several classes, but at different levels:

> a first introduction together with basic symbols,
> a greater grasp of concepts and vocabulary,
> an ability to make use of the ideas in new situations,
> an absorption of the ideas and language so that they are spontaneously used in mathematical activities.

It is an interesting approach which could well be developed and used elsewhere.

"Mathematical activity" is now much talked about and, rightly, given considerable attention. Those formulating national curricula have tried to take it into account in many ways. If one is offering advice or non–statutory guidance to teachers, then the matter is relatively straightforward. It is when one moves into the realms of statutory requirements that problems arise. Hungary places considerable emphasis on involving primary school pupils in activities which will help provide a foundation for future work in probability and combinatorics. In several grades these are not accompanied by formal targets for attainment. This can be seen as a very enlightened approach. However, it still presents difficulties in the area of teacher preparation, for it would seem essential that, associated with these activities, there are still clear "knowledge goals" which are perceived by the teacher and towards which students can be encouraged to progress. Activities cannot be allowed to degenerate into time-fillers from which children are expected to learn in a purely random manner. Otherwise, why come to school? Life is full of opportunities to learn about probability and much else in mathematics. (Yet, despite the fact that "chance" is all around us, we recall that the theory of probability was a relatively late entrant onto the mathematical scene.)

Understanding develops with use and in considering a curriculum we shall want to see how a pupil is helped to consolidate, revise, reinforce and deepen understanding. If, for example, a student is introduced to the concept of area through counting squares, when, and how, will that knowledge be used and developed, say, to encompass the use of formulae?

The need to revise is explicitly realised in the curriculum of Hungary where twenty or so periods are set aside each year for evaluation and recapitulation. More interestingly, half the time-tabled hours in the final year of the gymnasium are to be used for a systematic recapitulation of the whole course. This offers the opportunity (although we all know that such opportunities will not always be taken) not only to revise techniques before the school-leaving examination, but, more importantly, to review (or re-view) material with the advantage of mathematical hindsight – the material should now be seen from a new vantage point. Certainly, the decision to spend time in this way rather than to retain the teaching of the differential calculus within the curriculum is a most interesting and brave one.

The amount of time which is spent on a topic before a student moves on to something else, and the extent of new knowledge and the degree of mastery of it expected to have been shown before this occurs, is not something which can be readily inferred from a national curriculum. It is, of course, tied in with the manner in which the student is encouraged to consolidate knowledge. One inference drawn from the Second International Mathematics Study was that low attainment often had as a cause the too facile adoption of the "spiral" (or "helical") curriculum in which pupils constantly return to a particular topic, in theory at ever-increasing levels of depth and sophistication (McKnight et al, 1987, 97–99). Yet, if students do not carry understanding forward with them, then the "pillars" on which the helix is supported collapse, and the model degenerates into going round in circles. A guide to the extent to which this is a danger in any country will be the breadth of curriculum coverage in any one year. SIMS pointed to Japan as a country which appeared to provide a successful annual balance of range, depth and duration of coverage. Perhaps the reader would bear this thought in mind when studying the Japanese curriculum.

2.8 Teachers

It is universally accepted that schools exist to provide education for pupils. What is less than generally accepted is that they must also provide worthwhile and satisfying employment for teachers. If the latter is ignored, then teachers capable of implementing forward–looking and demanding curricula will simply fail to materialise.

Committees may draw up curricula, but it is teachers who make, or fail to make, them work. It is just as important, then, to consider the cognitive and administrative demands which national curricula make upon teachers, as the cognitive demands made upon students. Except as a purely academic exercise, a curriculum cannot be considered in isolation from the teaching force which must implement it.

Sometimes the strength of a teaching force within a country will allow developments which could not be considered elsewhere. Thus, in Denmark we find that the same teacher takes a particular class for all subjects for the first six years of primary/elementary school (ie up to age 12). It is considered that their initial training fits them for these demanding tasks. In Italy it is intended that there will be three teachers at each of the primary key stages (Grades 1,2 and Grades 3–5): one being a mathematics and science specialist. (In England only four per cent of primary school teachers have a main specialisation in mathematics and eleven per cent one in science.) The possible disadvantages for an individual pupil or teacher of the teacher being associated with a class for such a long period do not need stressing; neither, however, do the great advantages of a potentially much more integrated and co–ordinated primary school course, provided within a stable environment.

In a similar way, coordination of secondary–school mathematics and science teaching is facilitated in some countries, eg Italy, by having those subjects taught throughout a key stage by the same teacher. Ensuring a meshing between mathematics and other syllabuses is not easy, and whether the necessary degree of cooperation has been achieved cannot be readily judged by reading the mathematics syllabus in isolation. However, it is possible to note when such topics as displaying data, practical measurement, scientific notation, mensuration, presentation and manipulation of formulae, and compound measures (distance/time, etc), are introduced, and to see if the scientists' reasonable demands are likely to be met in a satisfactory manner.

What varies very much from country to country is the amount of professional responsibility given to, and expected from, teachers. The single, "state" text is now rarely to be found in the countries surveyed (but see Greece), so the choice of text, even if from a state-approved list, is one common responsibility. The freedom which a teacher has to vary or re-order content, and to change emphases, possibly by spending a longer or a shorter time on a topic, also differs. There are also different expectations concerning setting and marking homework, and time given to the preparation of lessons. The number of hours a week during which the teacher is expected to be in a classroom teaching varies considerably from country to country (see, for example, Section 3.6). Since it is usually defined in a teacher's terms of appointment, rather than in national curricula, it lies outside the scope of this book. Nevertheless, it is an essential factor which must be taken into account when discussing the feasibility of the practical implementation of a curriculum; so too must be the support facilities available in the way of in-service training, ancillary help, equipment and materials.

One of the teacher's greatest responsibilities, however, may well lie in the area of assessment, and it is to this that we now turn.

2.9 Assessment

Formal assessment of the work of students in school began in Prussia towards the end of the eighteenth century with the institution of the Abitur. The French 'bac' followed shortly afterwards and there the entrance examinations to the Grandes Ecoles added another dimension to assessment. A feature of the Abitur was that it was school-based. The French chose to exploit a new mode of examining -the written examination. For it must be remembered that until the late 1700s examinations within European universities had been entirely oral. The two traditions of oral and school-based examinations have persisted in a number of countries. Often, but not invariably, the final, school-leaving examination is centrally and externally directed, but it is unusual for a pupil to take external examinations at more than one age (but see Japan).

However, the fact that teachers overseas would look in amazement at externally directed testing at 7, 11, 14, 16 and 18 (plus 17 for some pupils) as is now to be the case in England, does not mean that student assessment plays little part in other systems. As readers of the second section will soon realise, in many countries the annual promotion of students is not taken for granted. There is a form of school-based annual "certification", and those not achieving the required standard must repeat a class (or pass resit examinations in the September before they can be promoted).

Assessment, then, is taken seriously and is seen as an important part of the teacher's craft. For example, in Luxembourg, the probationary teacher is tested on the correction and marking of students' work.

In most countries, examination systems have just "evolved", often from a model based on the Abitur or the bac, and traditions have died hard. One noteworthy feature of German examining is that the two southern Länder have much more centralised examining systems than the northern ones. The reason given for this is that, in the last century, teachers in the south did not enjoy the same social status as did teachers in Prussia. There were greater pressures on them, therefore, when they denied certification to students. As a result, they sought to shift responsibility for such assessment to a central authority: a nice example of how teacher status and the shouldering of responsibilities can interact.

Although most countries' assessment systems have evolved, the new system in England was designed by a committee which sought to meet constraints set by politicians. There, the setting out of statutory "assessment arrangements related to the 10 levels of attainment" will, if and when it occurs, forge a closer link between the national curriculum and assessment procedures than would appear to exist in any of the other countries described below. In fact, there are references to assessment in few national curricula. As a result, the information on assessment to be found in this book is usually based on information supplied by friends of the author.

Arguments can be advanced for a strongly-centralised school-leaving examination - it brings a desirable degree of homogeneity in its wake and can be used as a means for promulgating new developments. Yet the existence of such an examination is clearly neither a necessary nor a sufficient condition for the well-being of an educational system. More hope would seem to lie in helping teachers to articulate and accept clearer attainment objectives (in a broad sense), to exercise a variety of methods to assess the knowledge and attainments of their students, and to respond quickly and positively where there is a lack of progress. But that is easier said than done!

3

LESSONS TO BE LEARNED – A PERSONAL VIEW

This chapter differs greatly from others in this book. Elsewhere I have tried to write and to describe in an objective manner. I write 'tried', because any selection of data for presentation is bound to conceal a degree of subjectivity. Biases will become evident in the choice of vocabulary used to describe traits, or, say, in the way in which attention is drawn to particular features of a curriculum. Here, however, the views are personal, often refer specifically to England and Wales, and are in many cases controversial. In no way, then, is the chapter intended to present the views of the Mathematical Association or even of one of its committees. Yet I hope it will draw attention to certain issues concerning curriculum construction which every country must face. I shall have no complaints if my views are challenged in the same spirit in which this chapter is written. Progress comes through criticism and debate, rather than by unthinking acceptance.

3.1 The problems

First, consider some of the problems of English education which led in part to the imposition of a National Curriculum. (Here, I apologise to readers from the other parts of the UK, but the four divisions do not have identical problems – even if many are shared. For example, Scotland's continuation rates post–16 are much higher than England's, and Northern Ireland would seem to have higher average levels of attainment. However, attempts to provide evidence on all four systems would be very difficult.)

It is important to ask, what do students leave the system knowing and being able to do? What are their attitudes to education and the continuing need for it? Such questions are extremely difficult to answer, and we must fall back on some rather simplistic measures when we try to do so. However, it is obvious that the majority of English students have performed comparatively poorly in a sequence of international comparative studies (see, eg, Robitaille and Garden (1989), IAEP (1989) for data on mathematics). Also, compared with students in other leading, developed countries, relatively few choose to stay in school, or even take vocational training, beyond the age of compulsory schooling. What proportion of the population a nation wishes to retain in education post–16 is a matter of choice. Certainly, in the nineteenth century there was great opposition to over–educating the populace. However, the need for a developed country to have a numerate, literate, technologically capable and adaptable workforce is no longer in dispute.

A particularly worrying fact is that "average" and "below average" pupils within the English system appear to attain far less than do similar pupils in other major, educational systems. The percentage leaving school with low–level or no qualifications is also correspondingly high. (See, eg, Finegold et al, (1990).)

One would have expected, then, that a new national curriculum would have made a serious attempt to deal with the two problems:

(i) how to raise the attainment standards of the mass of pupils, and

(ii) how to create routes which would encourage more pupils to stay in education post–16.

3.2 The TGAT model

The basic features of the TGAT model (and the reasons for its name) are to be found in the national description for the United Kingdom. Briefly, panels set up to design curricula in the various subjects are required to divide curricular objectives, whether concerned with 'processes' or 'products', into a number of "attainment targets". Each target is further described by means of a number of "statements of attainment" which can be used to check on a pupil's progress. These statements, which can be viewed as a form of criterion–referencing, are allocated to one of ten levels. A student is expected to proceed through the levels in each attainment target at a speed appropriate to his or her ability. General guidance on the rate at which progress should be made is provided by a graph reprinted in the national description.

Before discussing the model in detail, one must consider its genesis.

For a number of reasons, including those outlined in the previous section, some political action to remedy shortcomings in the educational system had to be seen to be being taken. A national curriculum was the outcome. (This was, in fact, not unexpected; see, for example, Howson, (1982), p. 280.) In a sense this begged the more difficult problems of a demoralised, poorly–regarded teaching force (which, in particular, contained insufficient qualified teachers of mathematics), of run–down schools and of a society which put little value on education.

Indeed, this should have provided the country with the opportunity to think seriously about the aims of the English and other UK systems; to design a balanced school curriculum, appropriate for the year 2000, as well as suitable programmes of study for individual subjects; to set clear objectives for teachers, and to reconsider existing assessment procedures at all levels of education.

However, this opportunity was effectively denied us on two counts. One was that the timetable for implementation was based on political rather than practical considerations. The other that it was decreed, in an attempt to ensure that teachers would change their attitudes and procedures, that there would be externally-directed testing of all pupils at the ages of 7, 11, 14 and 16.

Externally-directed testing on this scale was something which had no parallels elsewhere. What were originally envisaged appear to have been paper and pencil tests of basics in English and Mathematics applied on a country-wide scale. However, similarities with the nineteenth century "payment by results" system seemed all too obvious to educators, who feared that such testing would limit teaching and so effectively restrict learning, particularly in the primary schools. In order to prevent this happening, the assessment system described above was devised. This placed equal emphasis (for pupils of all abilities) on all aspects of learning and on all subjects within the curriculum.

At great speed, the scheme received official approval and working groups were directed to design subject curricula around this framework. The proposals for assessment were extremely complex and, because of the administrative burdens they placed on teachers, have subsequently had to be recast. As a result, the intended balance between subjects has been impaired.

What went largely unquestioned at the time that the mathematics curriculum was being devised was the educational validity of the underlying model. For it can be argued that this is not only complex in practice, but also, so far as curriculum design is concerned, theoretically simplistic.

It is important, then, when considering the English national curriculum, to distinguish between problems which have arisen because of the manner in which the TGAT model has been implemented, and others inherent in that model. The former could, and should, be rectified in the short term, but are in some ways matters of national concern only. The problems of the model itself would seem of more general importance.

3.3 Problems of implementation

The working group established to prepare a national curriculum in mathematics made genuine efforts to deal with some of the key problems which faced it. Some of these are shared by mathematics educators everywhere: how to cope with the problem of children of different abilities who learn mathematics at very different rates and who are attracted by, or need to master, different aspects of the subject; how to incorporate the calculator and the micro into teaching; how to design a contemporary approach to the teaching of geometry and algebra; how to build probability and statistics into the curriculum; and how to ensure that more than lip-service is paid to the task of helping students use and apply that mathematics which they have learned. In addition, they were faced with a more "local" problem: that of ensuring that what they saw as good in English mathematics teaching was not forgotten in an attempt to remedy obvious weaknesses. All this was attempted.

Yet, it is easy to criticise the national curriculum in mathematics as contained in the statutory orders and summarised in this book. One can remark upon the eccentric placing of certain statements of attainment (eg, those relating to mensuration) and to questions of "pacing" (eg, the treatment of trigonometric functions for all angles). There are some strange orderings (eg, "interpret (7/3)x3 = 6.999999 if it occurs on a calculator" (level 4), and "explain that 0.23 is 2 tenths and 3 hundredths or 23 hundredths" (level 6)). Activities to be engaged in and encouraged are confused with attainments to be mastered. The choice, and even the mathematical accuracy, of some of the examples (see Howson 1989) can be questioned, as can the optimistic and untested assumptions concerning the teaching of probability. The "learning gradients" proposed at different stages (eg, contrast what is required for Level 7 with that for Level 8) would seem to differ markedly. That such examples are to be found in Parliamentary Orders is unfortunate, even, in some cases, astounding. It is not surprising, therefore, that significant, but still in my view insufficient, changes have been made in the more recent, Northern Ireland proposals.

It would seem essential that changes of detail should now be made without further delay to the statutory orders for England and Wales. If this is not done then, for example, 16–19 courses operative from 1994 will have to be built upon a very strange foundation. It has been officially proposed (SEAC, 1990) that such advanced courses should be designed to be suitable for those students who have only attained Level 7. What this means in mathematical terms can be inferred from the national description and the table in Chapter 2.

However, such changes within the existing framework will produce but limited results. There is a need to reconsider the validity of the underlying model.

3.4 Criticisms of the TGAT model

Any model used for curriculum construction must satisfy certain key demands. It has to cope with the problems of differentiation of curricula (not only content, but also presentation and timing), with those of the teaching and learning of mathematics, and with the constraints of external assessment.

The TGAT model (as used within mathematics) makes a remarkable assumption: that curricula can be independent of the student's age and ability. Differentiation through depth of treatment or expected outcome is largely ignored. Students of all abilities are expected to follow the same path – the only accepted variable is rate of progress. Thus, for example, the fact that a student is nearing the end of compulsory education is totally ignored. In particular, the need to prepare those of average attainment to undertake post–16 academic or vocational study is not specifically addressed. That is, the latter do not concentrate in Key Stage 4 (ages 14–16) on acquiring the pre-requisites for further study. Indeed, the programmes of study may well demand that they spend time on preparatory work for topics which they will never reach.

In Northern Ireland, this problem has been recognised and, to some extent, acted on. For example, "interpretation of a pay–slip" is statutory in Key Stage 4 for all pupils and is level independent. This might seem an unexciting response to the underlying problem, but, in fact, the Northern Irish go further: "the content [for Key Stage 4] is divided into two sections. One contains age-related material, which should be taught to all pupils during the Key Stage, to an extent commensurate with their abilities. The other section is set out by Level." The Northern Ireland proposals, therefore, clearly acknowledge that the "levels" model ceases to have validity in the later stages of compulsory education. Indeed, it could be argued that similar objections could be made at earlier key stages.

The English approach to curriculum specification has been tried before. The Hamilton Fyfe report (1947) described the results:

> *"Whatever be the values of the "subject" carried to its full term in university study, they cannot "be achieved for the child of 16 by simply snipping off a certain length of the 'subject' like a piece of tape." This is a point that needs to be stressed continually. Every course must have its own unity and completeness, and a proper realism requires that content and methods alike be so regulated as to reach their objective within the time available."*

It is now being accepted that the proposals for testing, assessment, reporting and moderation make unreasonable and indeed impossible demands on the classroom teacher. Some changes have already taken place, others doubtless will follow. Again, though, these are essentially matters of detail. It is more important to ask how the model will influence the way in which mathematics is taught and learned. For example, the suggestion that the curriculum can be adjusted in this way to cope with an individual pupil's rate of progress is unique to England. One result is that there may well be even more extensive use of individualised materials within schools. Here we see how the choice of model has, in this particular case, important implications for how the subject is taught.

So far as the learning of mathematics is concerned, the suggestion of a steeplechase over ten fences would seem altogether inappropriate. (When will "fell at level 4" or "refused at level 5" be seen in teachers' reports?) Ensuring that a subject is taught, or even that, on one occasion, certain attainments are achieved, is not the major problem. Rather, this lies in improving teaching and ensuring that, once taught, topics are constantly revised and reinforced – a weakness of the "levels" approach.

The model employed also affects how mathematics is viewed and how its teaching meshes in with that of other subjects.

As the Northern Ireland report says, the close link between the English programmes of study and the statements of attainment, "encourages a fragmentary approach to mathematics and it implies that what is taught and what is assessed are one and the same". This "fragmentation" occurs in various forms: through profile components, attainment targets and levels. The resulting "atomisation" is reminiscent of those exhaustive, and essentially profitless, taxonomies published in the USA in the 1970s.

Individually–determined progress within separate subjects can also lead to independent and non–supportive subject curricula. How can a quantitative science syllabus be planned and taught, if it is by no means certain to what mathematical content students have been introduced?

Even if programmes of study are provided similar to the Northern Ireland proposals for Key Stages 3 and 4, or, as in England, non–statutory guidance attempts to dissuade schools from adhering too closely to the levels model, then problems persist: the assessment procedures set out in orders will no longer be appropriate. If a topic is taught on the grounds that it makes sense for this to be in the programme of study for a particular key stage (as in Northern Ireland), then it would seem inappropriate not to assess it, in some way, at that time.

The manner in which statements of attainment are given obscures the fact that not all children will respond to a mathematical topic in the same way. The Secretary of State might well demand that "attainment targets and programmes of study should apply without modification to all pupils", but this shows an ignorance of what is possible and desirable. Northern Ireland calls for age-related material "to be taught to all pupils ... to an extent commensurate with their abilities". This approach, although at odds with the previous demand, offers more promise of educational success. It is, of course, a well-tried means of effecting differentiation.

Perhaps the greatest victim of the TGAT model has been the attempt to assess the pupil's ability to use and apply mathematics. The Mathematics Working Group's original proposals for doing this did not use the ten TGAT levels in the way then envisaged. Partly because of this, the proposals were rejected and an attempt was made to describe the group's objectives using the simplistic TGAT syntax. The results only demonstrate the inherent absurdity of the process. For example, the Northern Ireland proposals attempt to distinguish between strategies (Level 6), systematic strategies (Level 7) and efficient strategies (Level 8). Once again, "depth", "complexity" and "context" have been ignored.

One of the strongest features of English mathematics education has been the way in which attempts have been made to present mathematics in context and to encourage its use and application. Open-ended coursework, projects and investigations have been found in schools for many years. Yet by attempting to institutionalise these and to describe their desired outcomes in simplistic terms, are we not in danger of losing their essence? Are we falling into the same "assessment trap" as the politicians? Process criteria are extremely difficult to formulate and apply: is it realistic to ask for them to be defined within the 10-level framework?

It was emphasised in Chapter 2 that national curricula must be designed with the need for eventual change in mind. It is a problem which arises in every country and with respect to every curriculum model. However, the statutory, targets-and-levels framework is far too constraining and detailed to permit serious developmental work. At a preliminary stage, it is possible, as was done in Northern Ireland, to remove an attainment target here, and shuffle a few statements of attainment there, but once the system is in operation, how is change to proceed? How are textbooks to be trialled and produced? These questions have never been seriously and openly addressed, yet it is essential that answers to them are speedily found.

An interesting, shared problem concerns the place which experimental approaches should have in a statutory curriculum. We note, for example, how the English approach to algebra has moved away from the unsuccessful, traditional treatment still to be found in many countries. Yet, in some respects the move is to the experimental, the vague and the untested. How, within statutory frameworks, does one bridge the gap between the unworkable and the untried? In such cases might it not be better to specify desired end-points and indicate the amount of time which could profitably be devoted to the topic concerned in different grades?

A similar approach might well be adopted with respect to the micro. Rightly, the English curriculum developers, along with their peers in other countries, wish teachers to make effective use of the micro in their teaching. However, it is not clear at present how this can best be done. Perhaps the way ahead might be to insist that teachers use them in a considered manner and make a written report which can be discussed with local inspectors, colleagues in other schools etc. This could prove more profitable than statutorily linking the use of micros with specific attainment targets, particularly if these serve no obvious mathematical purpose.

It is essential also to ask what effect the adopted model is likely to have on pupil motivation. Here, it must be stressed that TGAT made a genuine attempt to deal with the problem of the low-attainer. However, the likely effectiveness of the proposed solution must be questioned.

The proposals will do little to encourage pupils to stay on in education. The emphasis on labelling children and publishing school results will tempt teachers to move brighter children through the levels in an over-ambitious and superficial manner. Legislating for a "seven year gap" at 11, although done with the best of intentions, is accommodating to the symptoms and not a cure for the underlying problem. The large rump of unmotivated low-attainers is unlikely to disappear.

The average attainer, too, will soon be left behind the high-attainer, with no clear mathematical pathway leading to further education. In some ways this is a result of the decision to look at 5-16 in isolation and not to see how this might provide a planned progression to post-16 education. We note that the national curricula for the other countries we describe cover all the years of schooling, not just the compulsory ones. Pre-15 or pre-16 courses are, ideally, planned either to be "terminal", ie self-contained, or to lead into well-defined senior-secondary or vocational school streams. Clearly, within England some new format must quickly be found for 16-19 mathematical education which preserves the standards expected of high-attainers whilst offering pathways to higher and further education for the average student. A review of the 5-16 programme will, however, be an essential prerequisite.

3.5 Some questions of content

> *"[The French curriculum is] smaller and less ambitious with respect to ... content than those of the majority of our geographic neighbours .. Whether that is a good or bad thing is open to discussion" (Legrand, 1988).*

> *"[The Cockcroft Foundation List and GCSE List 1] cover material [such as decimals and fractions, area and angle and number scales] ... included more because the authors believe they ought to be there rather than because they expect pupils can currently achieve the knowledge and understanding they involve." (Foxman et al., 1990)*

These two quotations illustrate some of the key problems of curriculum construction. Of course, a topic should only be included in a curriculum if there is evidence that it can be successfully learned by the target students. Here, however, we immediately meet problems. "Successful" under what circumstances? Is it, for example, reasonable to assume that what can be learned in Tokyo schools, can also be learned in those of London or Paris?

Clearly, the teacher and the motivation of the students are but two of the variables that affect what can successfully be taught and learned in the classroom. Such differences must influence national curricula. Yet experience in other countries cannot be totally ignored.

The English curriculum is a curious mixture of breadth and lack of ambition. So far as breadth of coverage is concerned, substantial demands are made of low–attainers. Yet anyone studying the curricula reprinted in this book will note just how low are English expectations for the below–average pupil in certain areas, particularly arithmetic, which other countries regard as basic. On the other hand, the table in Section 2.2 indicates that average pupils encounter most "basic" topics, with some notable exceptions, at about the same age as their international peers. Let us consider one such topic, decimals, in some detail.

Deficiencies in English pupils' knowledge of, and ability to use and interpret decimals have been highlighted in the studies of SIMS, IAEP and the Assessment of Performance Unit (Foxman et al, op cit). It is interesting to consider the differing responses one might make to this. One is vividly illustrated in Foxman (op cit). There it is argued (p. 24) that current attainment targets should be reviewed "against known levels of performance". In particular, it is reported that "at age 15 only half the pupils of average ability [in England, Wales and Northern Ireland] can correctly order decimals". The implication appears to be that, within the national curriculum, "read, write and order decimals" is misplaced at Level 6. It should be at a higher level and in a later programme of study.

It is, indeed, one way in which research results can be used when constructing a curriculum. However, is this not, again, merely accommodating to the symptom?

Other data emanating from the National Foundation for Educational Research allows us to see the problem in a different light. NFER (1989), reporting on the IAEP comparative study wrote: "There were six questions ... which involved decimals: the United Kingdom had by far the lowest success rate in each case. The US, the educational system with the second lowest mean score on the decimals sub-test, had a mean success rate of 58% - considerably higher than [the 37% of] the UK."

Clearly, targets for pupils' attainment should be linked to "known levels of performance". If, however, by this we mean what is currently being achieved in that country, then this will effectively rule out educational advance.

Reading, writing and ordering decimals is surely something that "ought to be there". If England lags behind the rest of the world in teaching this topic, then we must ask "why?", not merely neglect it.

Does the problem stem from:

(a) inefficient teaching,
(b) insufficient emphasis,
(c) an attempt to teach a formal idea too soon,
(d) an insufficiently detailed curriculum specification (in which only the end-point is noted and not the steps to be taken on the way), or
(e) a lack of motivation on the part of students?

Such questions must always be asked. They are not peculiar to England since the introduction of the National Curriculum. To help answer them, research findings are essential. These must, however, not be solely of an introverted type; comparative studies must be undertaken and their findings acted upon.

The question raised in the quotation from France which heads this section is one which must be answered in all countries. How broad should a curriculum be? Should relatively few topics be taught in some depth hoping for a considerable degree of understanding, or is it the aim to lay broad but comparatively shallow foundations? To what extent do the answers to these questions depend upon the type of student being considered? Moreover, such questions cannot be answered in isolation from expectations concerning retention rates in education. If students will almost certainly remain at school post–15 then the need for shallow introductions largely disappears. Thus the Japanese can hold trigonometry back until the senior high school (15+). In fact, a feature of many curricula during the last decade has been the elimination of much material. True, many now find a place for more probability and statistics, but this is often at the expense of many of the "modern maths" topics introduced in the 1960s, of formal geometry, and of algebra and trigonometry. As was written in the previous chapter, it is essential that students should take something forward with them from a series of lessons on a particular topic, even if they do not take with them everything that has been taught. Shallow treatments or the teaching of small gobbets of a topic, created more with the intention of defining ten levels than by teaching and learning considerations are unlikely to prove helpful. In particular, one must question the wisdom of offering low–attainers a broad, shallow curriculum which lacks clear objectives.

3.6 A new model for curriculum design

If the arguments in Section 3.4 are accepted, then it is essential that we in England adopt a policy on differentiation which will encourage the average and below–average attainer and will help lift levels of attainment through the educational system as a whole. In the national descriptions which form the second part of this book we can see how this problem has been tackled (or not!) in other countries.

For example, West Germany has a basically tri–partite system and the Netherlands a well–defined multilateral one: the curricula of both countries have many interesting features and both are often referred to as having high–performing systems.

Yet the problems of selection encountered in such systems remain considerable. Indeed, these proved a major impetus to the abandonment of tri–partite systems in England and elsewhere. The introduction of multilateral schools in England was urged by the Trades Union Congress as long ago as 1934. This possibility was considered by the Spens Committee (1938) which decided against it and supported the establishment of separate tri–partite schools. Where tri–partite and multilateral schools are long established, then acceptance of their shortcomings is easier. This is particularly so where problems of both early and late transfers are alleviated and, most importantly, where there are clear opportunities for further education for students from all the various streams or schools. Nevertheless, questions persist about "real parity in education or equality of opportunity" (TUC, 1934).

Not altogether surprisingly, therefore, when educators in Spain considered the form that their new secondary education system should take (Ministerio de Educacion y

Ciencia, 1987), they looked at the alternatives available and opted for comprehensive schools.

Spain, then, lays down a basic curriculum for all up to the age of 16. Yet as in so many other countries, special provisions are made for mathematics teaching. In this instance, schools are allowed to offer additional, optional mathematics courses for the higher attainers. An alternative approach to differentiation is to offer a basic course to all, together with extension work for high–attainers, but all within the same timetabled hours. Another approach is one, common course for all, for example, in France (to age 13, but soon to be 15), and, until age 14 (ie Grade 8), in Denmark, Hungary, Italy and Japan. This last is, therefore, an influential model. It is a model based on a most important assumption: to quote Stevenson et al (1990)

> *In Taiwan and Japan [primary school] teachers ... reject the idea that some children may be incapable of mastering the curriculum. ... Teachers recognize individual differences among students and may spend extra time with slower students or ask faster students to assist them, but they focus on teaching all children regardless of apparent difficulties ....*

A similar argument was always advanced in the USSR, which uses the model until 15. There, however, there was a clear political motivation, in particular the writings of Marx and Engels on ability. Recently, the idea of differentiated schools (in addition to the few "special schools" which already exist) has been aired.

Certainly, if this "comprehensive" model can be effectively adopted in schools, then the benefits are considerable. For example, the proportion of an age cohort prepared, ie, trained and willing, to proceed to the next stage of education is likely to be very high, and difficulties of selection are removed along with other attendant social problems. (We note, however, that in many countries which adopt this model, pupils may be forced to repeat years. One problem is removed at the expense of creating others. For, not only can retention lead to social difficulties, but, in the way that it "averages" across the whole curriculum, it does nothing to help pupils whose abilities are very different in different subjects. Here, "setting" offers advantages.)

Yet, these benefits demand corresponding commitments and sacrifices. Taiwanese and Japanese teachers, we are told, have more preparation time to deal with the demanding task of teaching mixed ability students than do teachers in the UK and USA. France has, as we have seen, opted for a slimmed–down curriculum to enable it to achieve its objectives.

Also, we note that in France additional time is available for remedial work. Here we see a very important difference between countries. Is extra time for mathematics made available to the high-attainers (as in, for example, Belgium) or to those who require it to keep abreast of their classmates? Clear arguments can be put forward to support either approach. However, the possibility of employing the French course of action appears to be rarely considered. Yet extra time for mathematics means less time for something else, and influences the balance of the curriculum as a whole.

If comprehensive curricula are over-ambitious then they are likely to create a bewildered, low-attaining rump. It is also the case that two countries with comprehensive curricula, Greece and Japan, are also two countries in which there is much out of school tutorial teaching. This last can be interpreted as a "good thing" - parents are showing an interest in ensuring that their children perform to state-determined standards - or, alternatively, as an unfortunate encroachment on childhood and adolescence. Once again, the "solution" of one problem has led to the creation of another.

The aim, sought by many, of offering distinctive curricula within a single institution has recently led to the establishment in Dutch-speaking Belgium of so-called "unitary" schools. These would appear to begin, in some senses, as comprehensives and then gradually take on the character of multilaterals. It is an interesting innovation which, if successful, could well be taken up elsewhere.

It must be kept in mind, however, that, whatever the model adopted, it is only the intended curriculum which is the same for all pupils. Teachers will always exercise their discretion over coverage and depth of treatment. Data from SIMS indicate that this was the case in all the countries included in that study.

If we in England are to change our curriculum model, then selecting an appropriate replacement will not be easy; many factors have to be considered.

Two current initiatives in England, the establishment of City Technology Colleges and the freedom given to schools to "opt out" of local control and possibly become selective, can be interpreted as a low-key attempt to reintroduce a tri-partite system of grammar, technical and "other" schools. This, move has, however, already become the subject of political debate. For differentiation not only refers to the classification of pupils. It can also mean differentiation in the provision of resources, both financial and human.

If England were to return to a tri-partite model, then presumably a new model for the curriculum would emerge as a matter of course. This, however, is unlikely to happen for some years, if at all. What steps, then, might be taken?

Perhaps consideration, so far as mathematics is concerned, might be given to adapting and developing the "nesting" model formerly used in England. Here, we think of the overall mathematics curriculum consisting of three strands: the basic, the subsidiary and the extra curriculum. This in some ways corresponds to the old model of Foundation list, List 1, and List 2. However, there are certain important differences. First, these curricula would be defined at all four key stages. Within a fixed time allowance, all students would be expected to cover the basic course. Here, "basic" is to be interpreted as what it is thought appropriate and possible for all students to learn. It must not be confused with the demands for "back to basics", neither must it be thought of as content to be taught and tested in a significantly different manner from that of the other curricula. The subsidiary curriculum would be followed by the majority of pupils and be designed to lead naturally into post-16 education. As in the case of the basic curriculum, its content would be statutorily defined. The extra curriculum, intended for high-attainers, would provide teachers with a large degree of choice. This would offer both professional rewards and also encourage curriculum development.

It is important, however, that the extra curriculum should not be seen as content to be tagged on "at the end of the course", ie, when all else has been completed. It should form part of the curriculum at every key stage. So, too, should the subsidiary curriculum. Teachers working within any key stage would, therefore, be encouraged to proceed horizontally through the different curricula, and not to hasten to work appropriate to the next key stage. The aim would be to offer enrichment to the high-attainers whilst not severing links between these and other students. The chance to "catch up" should be provided as late as possible.

One is still faced with the problem of the student who does not complete the basic curriculum of any key stage within the normal time allowed. There would seem three possible working solutions. That of retention is rarely used nowadays in England. As we have noted, this "solution" presents obvious problems, but still demands consideration. Another is partially to adopt the TGAT approach, and accept that it would be desirable for some students to be taught material from one stage below (or even possibly above) that normally to be expected. The third is to realise the importance of keeping abreast of one's peers in the basic mathematics curriculum and, as in France, to allot extra timetabled hours to remedial work.

Yet, whatever model is chosen, we must adopt procedures for student assessment which are not too demanding of time, or too limited in their aims, and which ensure that teachers see assessment as a vital part of their job. Such assessment, however, is not an end in itself. It must remain as a means to the end for which all teachers should be working: the effective education of all their pupils.

REFERENCES

Finegold, D., et al, 1990, *A British "Baccalauréat"*, Institute for Public Policy Research, London

Foxman,D., et al, 1990, *APU Mathematics Monitoring 1984–88 (Phase 2),* HMSO

Hamilton Fyfe Report, 1947, *Secondary Education,* HMSO, Edinburgh

Howson, A.G., 1982, *A History of Mathematics Education in England,* Cambridge University Press

Howson, A.G., 1989, "The Challenges and the Constraints", in Harding, D. and Hirst, K.E., *Mathematics 16–20,* Shell Centre, Nottingham University, 11–23

Howson, A.G. and Wilson, B.J., 1986, *School Mathematics in the 1990s,* Cambridge University Press

IAEP,1989, *A World of Difference,* ETS, Princeton

Legrand, M., et al, 1988, *Keep up with Teaching Mathematics in France,* Tangente, Paris

McKnight, C.C., et al, 1987, *The Underachieving Curriculum,* Stipes, Illinois

Ministerio de Educación y Ciencia, 1987, *Proyecto para la reforma de la enseñanza,* Madrid

NFER, 1989, *A World of Difference: a United Kingdom Perspective,* NFER, Slough

Robitaille, D.F., and Garden, R.A., 1989, *The IEA Study of Mathematics II: Contexts and Outcomes of School Mathematics,* Pergamon

SEAC, 1990, *Consultation on the Draft Principles for GCE Advanced Supplementary and Advanced Examinations,* SEAC

Spens Report, 1938, *Secondary Education with Special Reference to Grammar Schools and Technical High Schools,* HMSO

Stevenson, H.W., et al, 1990, *Making the Grade in Mathematics: Elementary School Mathematics in the United States, Taiwan and Japan,* NCTM

TGAT, 1988, *National Curriculum: a Report,* DES

Thom, R., 1973, "Modern Mathematics: Does it exist?" in Howson, A.G. (ed), *Developments in Mathematics Education,* Cambridge University Press, 194–209

Trades Union Congress, 1934, *Annual Report*

Travers, K. and Westbury, I., 1989, *The IEA Study of Mathematics I: Analysis of Mathematics Curricula,* Pergamon

Wolff, G., 1915, *Der Mathematische Unterricht der höheren Knabenschulen Englands,* Teubner, Leipzig

PART 2

BELGIUM

Age (yr)	Grade	
5-6	K	Nursery Education
6-7	1	Primary Education
7-8	2	
8-9	3	
9-10	4	
10-11	5	
11-12	6	
12-13	7	Secondary Education (Type I, Type II, Unitary)
13-14	8	
14-15	9	
15-16	10	
16-17	11	
17-18	12	

(Double lines indicate the start and end of compulsory education.)
Notes

1. Over 90% of children aged 3+ attend nursery schools.

2. Secondary education is offered in three types. Type I (state, local authority, and half the religious (Roman Catholic) schools) offer differentiated courses from 14; Type II (mainly church schools) differentiate into four streams (classical humanities, modern studies, technical, and vocational) from 12. The first three of these streams can all lead into higher education. In Flanders, a third type of school (unitary) is now replacing the Roman Catholic Type I and Type II schools. The change began in September 1989 in Grade 7 and will take six years to work through the system.

3. The Type I system permits children to switch streams (occasionally at the cost of 'repeating' a grade in the new stream).

4. Education is compulsory to 18. However, from 16 vocational education can be combined with part–time work (viewed as a complementary activity rather than independent employment).

BELGIUM

The Belgian school system is a very complicated one with many divisions. The most significant of these is the linguistic split, for there are two educational boards – one for the Dutch–speaking community, the other for French–speakers and the small, German–speaking community. Another division concerns 'control', for some schools are controlled directly by the government, others by local authorities (eg, provinces, towns), and very many (about ¾ in Flanders and ½ in French–speaking Belgium) by private bodies (almost exclusively religious groups).

In theory only the state schools are bound by the governmentally prescribed national curricula. However, almost all schools receive some funds from the state and must submit to a degree of state control, although this still allows them some curricular freedom.

As already indicated, secondary education in Flanders can take a variety of forms. Type I schools are now in the majority. In these schools the six years of secondary education are divided into three two–year stages. The first stage (12–14), the 'observation level', is basically common. Those who performed badly at primary school but who now show signs of marked improvement can spend three years over this stage before joining the second–stage technical or academic streams. The second stage (14–16), the 'orientation level', is basically tripartite (academic, technical,vocational), as is the final, 'determination' level. The number of hours per week to be spent studying mathematics varies substantially. (Even at the first level there is some variation in the number of hours per week, for, in addition to the compulsory four hours a week those 'who want to deepen their understanding' may study for a further two hours per week, provided the school is able to mount such an option.)

Type II schools (which reflect more traditional educational patterns) offer more clearly differentiated courses. Divisions are made at age 12 and within the four 'directions' (each with at least three 'sub–directions') mathematics plays vastly different roles. Thus it is emphasised strongly (eight hours per week or even more) in the Latin–Maths sub–direction of the classical humanities stream, or the Sciences A sub–direction of the modern studies stream; but less so in Greek–Latin, Sciences B, or in the Technical and Vocational streams.

It is intended that all secondary schools in Flanders will switch gradually to Type III, or Unitary, schools. These will be basically comprehensive /multipartite, but with some interesting curricular features. In particular, the following will be legislated centrally:

> the maximum number of hours of teaching a week;
> the minimum number of hours of teaching per week to be shared by all pupils (this number decreases through the grades);
> the courses which have to be taught in common and the minimum number of hours per week.

These regulations will apply to the four streams to be found within the unitary schools: common, technical, arts and vocational.

The secondary schools in French-speaking Belgium are of type I and type II form and have similar characteristics to their Flemish counterparts. However, few type II schools remain in French-speaking Belgium (they exist mainly in large towns such as Brussels), and the proportion of such schools is a major difference between the two systems.

The curriculum for the Dutch-speaking primary schools was published in two parts, the first appearing in 1977, the second in 1980. The method of presenting the syllabus is of considerable interest (and in my experience unique). Alongside the description of mathematical content is not only an indication of the grades in which it is expected that the material will be treated, but also the cognitive level to be reached in any particular grade. The levels, I–IV, range from I, a first introduction together with basic symbols (eg those for the union and intersection of sets), to II, a greater grasp of concepts and vocabulary (equality of sets, singleton, function), to III an ability to make use of the ideas in a new situation, and IV an absorption of the ideas and language so that they are spontaneously used in mathematical activities. Thus, to take an example, the use of arrow diagrams, to illustrate relations such as 'weighs more than' on a set of children, is classified as II, II, III, III, III, IV respectively for the six grades. The syllabus provides guidance on what is considered a 'minimum' approach and advises of the need for differentiation.

The detail in which the syllabus is given is too great to be reproduced here. Summarised it is (grades in brackets):

Sets, introduction (1), operations and Venn diagrams (2,3), relations (1–6), reflexivity, etc. (4), function (and the language of functions) (6). **Numbers**, small naturals (1), names (ordinal and cardinal) (1), negative numbers (temperature, etc.) (3–4), naturals up to 1000 (2), 10000 (3), reading and writing any natural (4), decomposition into powers of 10 (3–5), roman numerals (4–6), number line (4,5), congruences (4,5), factorization of numbers less than 21 (1,2), less than 100 (2,3), primes less than 100 (3,4), factorization into primes less than 1000 (4–6), gcd (3–5) (of more than two numbers (4–6)), rules for divisibility by 2, 5, 10 (3,4), 4, 25, 100 (4,5), 3, 9 (5,6). **Fractions** (rationals), introduction (shading areas) (2,3), ordering and equals (same denominators) (3,4), on number line (4,5), simplification (3–5), mixed fractions (4,5), decimals (4,5), recurring (4–6), converting (4,5), percentages (5,6), negative rationals (4,5). **Operations** with numbers, addition of small numbers (1,2), of three or more (1–3), subtraction as inverse (1–3), numerical equations with frames (1–3), 'vertical' addition (3 digits) (3,4), subtraction (3 digit) (3,4), addition and subtraction of vulgar and decimal fractions (3–6), tables (1–6), multiplication (1–3), division (2–4), associativity of multiplication (2–5), distributivity (1–6), expressing as a product of factors (3–5), divisors of numbers up to 100 (2,3), over 100 (3–6), gcd of 2 or more numbers (4–6), multiples of small numbers (1–3), lcm of 2 or more numbers (4–6), long multiplication (4–6), ratio (5–6). **Structure**, mappings, operations tables, clock arithmetic (2–6). **Logical vocabulary**, 'and', 'or', 'not', 'true', 'false' (1–5), 'all', 'the least'. 'the greatest' (3–6), 'if... then' (5–6). **Processes**, hypothesising, experimenting (1–6), symbolizing (5,6), schematising (3–6). **Applications**, money and buying (1–3), percentage (4,5), interest (5,6), length, area, volume, weight, capacity, temperature, time (1–6), data, mean (5,6), simple chance (6). **Measure**, concept (1–6), length (m, dm, cm) (1–3), mm (4,5), area (1–5), own units (3,4), cm^2, m^2 (3–6), km^2, mm^2 (5,6), squared paper (3–6), simple shapes (3,6). **Volume** (1–4), informal units (1–4), metric units of capacity (3–5), of volume (m^3, etc) (5,6), relations between (5), formula for simple shapes (cuboid, right prism, etc) (6). **Mass**, units (1–5), weighing,... (1–5), **Money**, francs (1), notes up to 100F (2), up to 5000 F (3). **Time**, (1–3), units (hours, minutes,...) (1–4), days, weeks, ... (2–4), reading minutes and seconds on a clock (3–5). **Temperature**, warm, cold, ... (1–4), Celsius (2–4), graphs (2,6). **The metric system**, prefixes (kilo, hecto,..., milli) (5), ordering (5), decomposition (10.5m = 10m + 5dm, etc.) (4,5), mixed quantities, (speed, inhabitants per square km, etc.) (3–6). **Mensuration of plane figures**, concept of perimeter (2), simple polygons (3,4), concept of area (2–4), rectangle (4), using compositions and decomposition (eg rectangles with triangles cut away from corners) (5,6), areas of simple similar figures (5,6), parallelogram, triangle (5,6), trapezium, regular polygon, circle (6), surface area of right prism, cylinder, pyramid (6), concept of angle (2,3), simple properties of angles (2–6), degrees (5), construction of special angles (45°, 90°,...) (5,6), concept of distance (as bird flies, 'taxi' metric) (3), point to a line, between two parallel lines (5), point from a plane (height of pyramid) (6). **Space**, left, right, above, below, inside, outside,... (1), concept of reflection (1–3), images (using carbon paper, pricking, etc.) (1–3), properties of two corresponding figures (using pin board, squared paper, miramath, etc.) (2–6), differences of properties of two figures **not** mirror images (2–6), symmetry (3–6), translation as a vector (4), invariance of properties under translation (5,6), rotations (5,6). **Figures and shapes** (1–6) (this section is described in great detail and mainly collects together geometrical concepts already described above.)

So far as the secondary level is concerned, the variety of curricula on offer stands in the way of a general description. Accordingly what is first described is the proposed syllabus for the first level (12–14) in the new, type III Dutch-speaking schools. These syllabuses will illustrate current thought on curricular matters. What we describe refers mostly to the Free (Catholic) Schools. There are some slight differences in the curricula of the Community (State) Schools. The stipulated hours of mathematics teaching per week in these are: Grade 7 5 hours, Grades 8–9 4 hours, Grade 10 3 or 5 hours, Grades 11–12 0, 2, 4, 6 or 8 hours. Set theory and relations are only implicitly mentioned and their teaching is not emphasised; 'Arithmetic' is not included in Year 4 (Grade 10); only the 2 hours a week option in Grades 11 and 12 offers a choice of topic, the programmes for the other courses are all fixed (the 6 and 8 hour options include Boolean algebra).

The syllabuses are presented in the following way (the examples refer to the 12–13 syllabus): first the goals are set out in a concise form (general goals, then those related to sets and relations, number and geometry). Goals are next set out in a differentiated form, ie it is clearly indicated whether a goal is 'basic', to be sought by all (eg the four operations on the rationals written either as vulgar fractions or in decimal form) or is an option for those students able to go further (eg equivalence relations and classes, rules for divisibility by 2, 4, 5, 25, 3, 9 and 11, gcd's and lcm's of two natural numbers). The goals are then 'concretised' (again in differentiated form – basic and extension). Methodological advice is then given, including suggestions for time allocation (a maximum of 25% for sets and relations, about 50% on number, and at least 25% on geometry).

Below we give the 'differentiated' goals ('B' indicates basic, 'E' extension). Some idea of the way in which the 'concretisation' works can be gained from the fact that the three sections 1.1 to 1.3 are restated as 44 more concrete objectives (16 of which are classified as 'basic').

Year 1 (12–13, four hours per week)

1. Sets and relations

1.1 (B) Sets; equality of sets, subsets of a set; intersection, union and difference of sets; product set.

1.2 (B) Relations; inverse of a relation; function, transformation; representation of a relation.
1.3 (E) Equivalence relations, equivalence classes, order relations.

2. Numbers

2.1 (B) The sets N, Z and Q; subsets; absolute value, ordering; the number line, place value.
2.2 (B) The four operations with integers.
2.3 (E) Divisibility in N : division, terminating or not, divisors, multiples; composite and prime numbers; expressing a natural number in prime factors, rules for divisibility by 2, 4, 5, 25, 3, 9 and 11; gcd and lcm of two natural numbers.
2.4 (B) The four operations with rational numbers written in fractional form and in decimal form.
2.5 (B) Properties of the operations; commutativity, associativity, distributivity.
2.6 (E) Powers with natural exponents, square roots.
2.7 (B) First degree equations with integer coefficients.
2.8 (B) Problems (applications).

3. Geometry

3.1 (B) Construction of parallel lines, perpendicular lines, angles, plane figures.
3.2 (B) Plane figures, identification and classification. Definition and properties.
3.3 (B) Lines and axes of symmetry in plane figures.
3.4 (E) Parallel projection.
3.5 (B) Problems involving the perimeter and area of a plane figure.
3.6 (B) Methods for finding the volume of a solid.

Year 2 (13–14) At this stage, two syllabuses (a) and (b) are offered. Here we list the fuller syllabus (ie, (a)). Topics shown in square brackets are omitted from syllabus (b).

1. Number

a. Properties of the sum and product in Q .
b. Powers with natural [integer] exponents and with exponent −1, integer powers of 10, scientific notation, [rules for operations with exponents].
c. Monomials and polynomials.
d. Remarkable products: $(a+b)^2$, $(a+b)(a-b)$; decomposition into factors.
e. Linear equations with one unknown.

f. Proportion.
g. Problems.

2. Geometry

a. Relative position of two straight lines: parallel and perpendicular. Length and angle, operations on angle measure.
b. Transformations of the plane: line and point reflections, translation and rotation, invariants, image of a figure.
[c. Congruence: congruent figures, congruence rules for triangles without proof].
d. Study of properties of plane figures; line intersecting parallel lines – angle properties, mediator and bisector as geometric loci; properties of sides, angles and diagonals of quadrilaterals – symmetry.
e. Constructions in connection with b, [c] and d.

As stated earlier the syllabuses given above for the first (Observation) level are those shortly to be implemented. Below we give existing syllabuses for Type I schools in Dutch–speaking Belgium. (The syllabuses for Type II schools differ only slightly.)

The Second Level (Orientation level, 14–16)

At the second level the pupils have a choice between three or five hours of mathematics a week.

Year 3 (14–15)

The fundamental contents are the study of the rational and real number systems, the cartesian equation of the straight line and, in geometry, properties of the triangle and the circle. Additional topics in the five hour option are transformations (isometries) of the plane, with applications in problem solving. We list here the programme for the five hour/week option.

I Arithmetic

Properties of the rational and real number fields with applications: square roots, remarkable products, decomposition in factors, solving linear equations and inequalities, use of the calculator.

II Cartesian equation of the line

Coordinates of a point, linear equations in two variables, graphical representation, straight lines through given points or with given directions, systems of two equations with two unknowns.

III Geometry

(a) Distances and angles, orthogonality;
(b) transformations of the plane: translations, projections, reflections, rotations, isometries;
(c) effect of transformations on the properties of plane figures (triangle, quadrangle, circle);
(d) congruencies;
(e) similarities and homotheties;
(f) Pythagoras's Theorem;
(g) sine, cosine, tangent, applications in right-angled triangles.

Year 4 (15–16)

In the fourth year, trigonometry also includes arbitrary triangles. In algebra skills in calculations with roots and exponents are trained. The most elementary notions of function theory are introduced through polynomial functions of the first, second and higher degree.

In the five hour/week option additional topics are: the scalar product, equation of the circle, divisibility and prime factors. The notion of proof is developed through problems and examples. Again, we list below the contents of the five hour option.

I Trigonometry

Sine, cosine and tangent of an angle in an arbitrary triangle: sine– and cosine–rules, applications.

II Geometry

Euclidean distance between two points, scalar product of vectors, orthogonality of straight lines, distance of a point to a line, equation of a circle.

III Arithmetic

Divisibility theory in the integers, prime numbers, decomposition in prime numbers, decomposition in prime factors, gcd, lcm. Operations with rational exponents.

IV Real function theory

(a) The linear function $y = ax + b$: zeros, increasing or decreasing functions, positive or negative values, solution of equations and inequalities.
(b) The quadratic function $y = ax^2 + bx + c$: zeros, sum and product of the roots, decomposition in factors, positive and negative values, graphical representations, quadratic equations and inequalities.
(c) Polynomial functions: zeros, divisibility by $(x - a)$, positive and negative parts, solution of inequalities.

The Third Level (Determination level, 16–18)

At the third level (fifth and sixth years) the pupils who have chosen the three hour/week option in the second level may choose now a programme with two or four hours/week of mathematics; those who had the five hours/week option choose a four, six or eight hour/week programme.

In the two hour option an intuitive, less formal teaching style is emphasized with a trend towards applications. Teaching shifts gradually to a more formal and deductive style as the number of hours increases.

The fifth year lays the fundamentals of (real) function theory which is more fully developed in the sixth year. Moreover in this last year a large number of optional topics is available.

Year 5 (16–17)

I Two Hour Option (50 hours of teaching/year).

(a) rational functions;
(b) continuity, limits, derivatives, polynomial functions.

II Four Hour Option (100 hours of teaching/year).

(a) and (b) above with

(c) irrational functions, trigonometric formulae and functions, with the calculus of limits and derivatives.

III Six Hour Option (150 hours of teaching/year).

(a) to (c) above with
(d) some topological ideas concerning the Euclidean line and plane and their applications in rigorous proofs;
(e) matrix calculus, linear systems;
(f) complex numbers.

IV Eight Hour Option (200 hours of teaching/year).

(a) to (f) above with
(g) vector spaces (low dimensional);
(h) geometry of three dimensions.

Year 6 (17–18)

I Two Hour Option

The programme consists entirely of options to be chosen from;

(1) function theory (rational functions, graphs, extremal values, definite integrals);
(2) the logarithmic and exponential functions;
(3) trigonometry;
(4) matrices and linear systems;
(5) geometry (three dimensional);
(6) logic;
(7) financial algebra (interest, etc.);
(8) descriptive statistics;
(9) algorithms.

(Teachers select 2 or 3 units depending upon the orientation of the school and their, or their students, preferences. The number of units selected will be proportionately greater in the 4 and 6 hour options.)

II Four Hour Option

Topics (1) to (3) above are compulsory and extended (eg with the indefinite

integral); 25% of the time is available for optional topics, to be chosen from
(4) matrices and linear systems;
(5) analytical geometry (conics);
(6) complex numbers;
(7) to (9) as above.

III Six Hour Option

The compulsory part of the program comprises topics (1) to (3) as for the four hour option, together with the study of real vector spaces and 3-dimensional geometry.

The optional part (25% of the time) can be chosen from

(1) analytical geometry (conics);
(2) combinatorics and probability;
(3) descriptive statistics;
(4) algorithms.

IV Eight Hour Option

All topics are compulsory.

(1) analysis; study of rational, irrational, trigonometrical functions; extremal values; the definite and indefinite integral; methods for determination of primitive functions; the logarithmic and exponential functions; sequences and series; numerical analysis.
(2) analytical geometry; the Euclidean, affine and projective plane; conics; geometrical loci; polar coordinates.
(3) combinatorics and probability.

French-speaking Belgium

Because of the shortage of space, details of the primary school curriculum in French-speaking Belgium have had to be omitted.

The secondary school syllabuses for French-speaking Belgium were drawn up from 1978 onwards by a committee representative of all types of schools. As a result, they are followed in all French-speaking schools.

The number of 'hours' (50 minute periods) of mathematics per week is:

Grades 7–8	(observation grades) 4
Grades 9–10	(orientation grades) 4 or 6 in general schools; 2 to 5 in technical vocational schools
Grades 11–12	(determination grades) 3 or 5 or 7 in general school, 2 to 5 in technical vocational.

The curricula in the vocational schools are not divided according to years but are given in six levels. The 'levels' correspond to different teaching groups and students may switch from one level to the following one during, or at the end of, the school year, or may be required to repeat a 'level' the following year (whilst progressing with the class in other subjects).

The syllabuses for the general secondary schools are presented in the following way:

(a) an introduction stating general objectives and goals,
(b) statements concerning particular topics (eg algebra, geometry),
(c) the contents presented in three columns, 'matière', 'savoir–faire', 'indications méthodologiques',

(corresponding, roughly, to notions, activities, and pedagogical hints)
or, more usually, in two: 'material' and 'commentary'.

A brief description of the curriculum is as follows (note that there are no 'B' or 'E' indications):

Grade 7 (age 12–13)

1. Natural numbers and positive decimals, the four operations, powers with natural exponents, inequalities and equalities.
2. Integers, absolute value, three operations, exact quotients.
3. Sets, member of, subset of, conditions in one variable, intersection, union, complement.
4. Conditions in two variables, pairs, relations, reciprocals, cartesian product, functions, bijection.
5. Geometry: incidence, parallelism (points, lines and planes), intersection of planes and lines, perpendicularity of lines; symmetries, axes, centres, segments of equal length, angles of equal measure, triangles, parallelograms, trapezoids, parallelepiped, cubes; image of a figure under a translation, reflection, rotation.

Grade 8 (age 13–14)

Numbers

1. Operations on real numbers, –x and 1/x , differences and quotients, rules for computation, linear equations in one unknown.
2. Numbers and lines, position, the number line, relation between the bijection **R** → line, translation and homothety.
3. Order on line and in **R** , first order inequalities.
4. Fractions, computation rules.
5. Powers, natural exponents, computation rules, powers of 10 with negative exponents.

Geometry

1. Transformations, reflections, translations, rotations, invariants.
2. Properties of figures, figures with line, point and circular symmetry, figures invariant under translations, triangle inequality, intersections of circle and line and of two circles, properties of triangle, quadrilateral, circle, angle sum, perpendicular bisectors, angle bisectors, right–angled triangle and circle, inscribed and circumscribed circles to a triangle, segment linking midpoints of two sides of a triangle.
3. Thales' theorem, homotheties, parallel projection.

Grade 9 (age 14–15)

Basic (4 hour) course

Algebra

1. Computations in **R** , literal expressions (formal treatment), square root, factorization, application to fractions.
2. First degree equations and inequalities, linear (affine) functions, zeros, transformation of formulas.
3. Simultaneous equations in two unknowns, systems of two equations.
4. Graphical representation of functions from the reals to the reals.
5. Polynomials, degree, sum and product.

Geometry

1. Isometries, invariants, congruent triangles, area of triangle and polygon.

2. Homotheties, definitions, invariants.
3. Projections, Thales, sine, cosine, tangent for right-angled triangle.
4. Pythagoras.

Enriched (6 hour) course

Algebra

1. Computations in **R** , rationals and non-rationals, properties of **R** , groups, order, literal computations.
2. Powers, integer exponents, square roots.
3. Approximations for sums, products, squares, square roots.
5. Factorisation with application to fractions with polynomial terms.
6. Equations and inequalities of the first degree in one or two unknowns.
7. Vectors: translations, addition, scalar multiplication, plane with origin.

Geometry

1. Isometries, composition, direct and opposite, special cases, congruent triangles.
2. Homotheties, Thales, invariants, similar figures.
3. Trigonometry of right-angled triangle, orthogonal projections.
4. Pythagoras.

Grade 10 (age 15-16)

Basic (4 hour) course

Algebra

1. First degree equations and inequalities in one unknown, $ax+by+c = 0$, simultaneous equations in two unknowns.
2. Square roots, $x \rightarrow ax^2+bx+c$, quadratic equations and inequalities.

Geometry and trigonometry

1. Vectors, translations, addition, scalar multiplication, bound vectors, linear combinations of vectors, basis, coordinates, vector representation of a line, scalar product, Pythagoras, orthonormal basis.
2. Radians, cotangent, 'associated angles', special values (30°,...), sine rule.

Enriched (6 hour) course

Algebra

1. Approximations for the quotient of two reals, equivalence of equations and inequalities.
2. Basic algebra plus graphs and representation, equivalence of systems, 3 equations in 3 unknowns and graphical representation.

Geometry

1. Transformation groups, invariants, similarities as transformations.
2. 2 and 3 dimensional vector spaces, linear combinations, dependence and independence, vector lines, vector equations, basis, coordinates, parametric and cartesian equations of a line, scalar product, Euclidean vector space, metrics (equalities in triangle and circle), scalar product in an orthonormal basis, applications.

Trigonometry

Oriented angles, sum, group, angle measure, relations in right–angled triangle, in other triangles, resolution of triangles (sine and cosine rule), trigonometric functions of a real, simple equations (inverse functions), scalar product and cosine.

Algorithmic computations

This section contains no new content but reminds the teacher of the need to build the calculator and micro into other curricular work.

Grade 11 (age 16–17)

At this level three mathematics options are offered taking, 3, 5 and 7 periods per week, which we shall denote below by A, B and C respectively. To conserve space we amalgamate the syllabuses for the A and B courses – the letters following any topic or group of topics indicating in which courses it is/they are contained.

A and B courses (3, 5 periods per week)

Real valued functions of a real variable: domains, growth, zeros, powers with real exponents, limits (A, B), continuity (B), asymptotes, (horizontal, vertical, oblique) (A, B), continuous functions (A), intermediate value theorem, differential calculus (definition, computation, usual formulae, slope of tangent, growth in an interval, maxima and minima, graphical representation) (B), trigonometric functions, periodicity (A, B), simple equations and inequalities (A), addition, multiplication and division formulae (B), equations and inequalities (B), derivatives of trigonometric functions (B), less formal approach to differentiation (but including max and min, and graphical representation) (A), planes and lines in space, intersections, parallelism, perpendicularity, distance, vectors, scalar products, orthogonality, norm, statistics (class, frequency, mode, mean, median, quartiles, variance, standard deviation, interquartile range) (B).

C course (7 periods per week)

Properties of the reals, sequences (AP and GP), graphical representation, domain, growth, composition, reciprocal, even and odd, periodic, continuity, limits, asymptotes, differentiation, derivatives, geometric and physical interpretation, properties, computations (four operations and composition of functions), Rolle's Theorem, mean value, Lagrange, first and second derivatives, growth, max and min, points of inflection, concavity, study of functions, derivative of reciprocal function. Trigonometric functions and inverses, addition, multiplication and division formulae, $a\cos x + b\sin x = \ldots$, other common formulae, equations, differentiation of trig functions. Lines and planes, parallelism, intersections, projections, Thales, perpendicularity, orthogonal projections, distance, skew lines, perpendicular bisector of a segment, intersection of spheres, lines, planes, angles between lines and planes, bisection of a dihedral. Translations and vectors, space with origin, real vector space, linear dependence and independence, sub-spaces, generators, basis, dimension, coordinates, sum and intersection of sub-spaces, linear sub-varieties, linear maps, characterisation by image of a basis, matrix representation, matrix computations, scalar product in 2 and 3 dimensional spaces, orthogonal transformations, affine and metric bases, vector, parametric and cartesian equations of lines and planes. Mean, mode, variance, standard deviation of finite samples, probabilities on a finite set, notion of probability, evaluation of probabilities.
Algorithms: sequences, limits, derivatives, graphical representation, roots of an equation, max and min, statistics.

Grade 12 (age 17–18)

A and B courses (3, 5 periods per week)

Statistics ((A) as for Grade 11 (B)), probability, events, compatible events, addition of probabilities, dependence, multiplication of probabilities (A, B), conditional probability (B), combinations, permutations (B).

Reciprocal of a function, derivative (A, B), inverse trig functions (B), exponentials and logarithms, properties, derivatives, e, integral of a continuous function (primitives) (A, B).
Conics (circle, ellipse, hyperbola, parabola as geometric loci), canonical equations, analytic geometry in 3–D, equations of lines, planes, spheres (B)

Either polar coordinates **or** complex numbers **or** matrix algebra (B).

C course (7 periods per week)

Integral of a continuous function, properties, Mean value theorem, primitives, simple computations, geometrical applications, natural logarithms (definition, properties, graph, other bases), isomorphism of positives under multiplication to reals under addition, exponential function (definition, properties, graph), a^x, inverse relationship, Maclaurin series.
Determinants (2 x 2 , 3 x 3) , det and linear dependence, rank of a matrix, simultaneous linear equations, compatibility, parallelism and perpendicularity of planes.
Complex numbers, definition, $r(\cos\theta + i\sin\theta)$, computations, de Moivre, n^{th} roots of unity.
Cartesian and polar coordinates, change of basis, problems on points, lines and circles, parametric and cartesian equations of geometric loci, ellipse and hyperbola (bifocal definition, axes of symmetry, parametric equation, directrices, asymptotes), parabola (focus–directrix, canonical and parametric equation, construction), intersection of lines and conics, tangents to a conic, polar equations of conics, simplification of general second degree equation, equation of hyperbola with respect to its asymptotes.
Problems with arrangements, permutations, combinations, binomial theorem.
Probability, evaluation, independence, conditional probability, simple laws, mathematical expectation, variance of a random variable.
Algorithms: numerical integration, solution of $f(x) = 0$, simultaneous equations in n unknowns.

DENMARK

Age (yr)	Grade		
5-6	K	Pre-school education	
6-7	1		
7-8	2	Folkeskole (Comprehensive primary and lower secondary education)	
8-9	3		
9-10	4		
10-11	5		
11-12	6		
12-13	7		
13-14	8		
14-15	9		
15-16	10		
16-17	11	Gymnasium (Upper secondary)	Folkeskole
17-18	12		Vocational and Technical
19-20	13		

Notes

1. Pre-school education is provided by the state and is attended by almost all 5 year-olds.

2. The Danish system is strictly comprehensive with unstreamed classes throughout Folkeskole. A 10th school year (Grade 11) is also offered within the basic Folkeskole.

3. About one third of the age cohort attend a Gymnasium and a further 50% or so remain in education after the school-leaving age of 16.

4. Parallel to the Gymnasium, and using the same teachers, is a 2-year course leading to the 'higher preparatory certificate' intended for mature students (cf. Portugal).

5. New structures for the Higher Preparatory Examination, which gives access to higher education, and for technical and vocational secondary education are being devised and will come into effect within a few years.

DENMARK

Several features of the Danish educational system set it apart from those of other EC countries. We note that compulsory education begins later than elsewhere and also that, up to Grade 10, the state schools (attended by about 90% of children) are not merely "comprehensive", but fiercely so. More significantly, there are important educational emphases, for example, an aim is to give each class the same "class teacher" throughout the whole or greater part of the nine (or ten) years of schooling. The class teacher, then, has an important role to play in watching over and guiding the development of individual children. The training of teachers is such that all are expected to be able to cope with teaching mathematics up to and including Grade 8.

The pupil's role and autonomy are also very different in Denmark from other countries – at least, in theory. According to the Folkeskole Act of 1975, each pupil " has not only the right but the obligation to take part in the democratic process of decision–taking in collaboration with the teachers on the question of the content, form and method of their learning within the given guidelines [setting out goals, a recommended syllabus and a time allocation for subjects] ". To facilitate this process, the weekly timetable must include a period for such discussions. Pupils' councils are now obligatory at all schools catering for 5th class (Grade 6) students or higher. Such councils represent pupils' interests to local education authorities.

Certifying external examinations are offered by the Folkeskole at two levels, the Leaving Examination (taken at the end of either the 9th or the optional, 10th year of the Folkeskole) and the Advanced Leaving Examination, taken after the 10th class. Examinations are not compulsory, but are normally taken in mathematics.

There is a 10–point marking scale divided into three main bands : excellent, average and weak. For entry to the gymnasium, students must be certified by the Folkeskole and must have satisfactorily passed the written leaving examination in Danish, mathematics and any other subjects required for the 'line' which they wish to follow in the gymnasium.

Mathematics must be studied in the nine classes of compulsory education. In the optional 10th year it is no longer compulsory for individual students, but every school must offer it. The time allocation for mathematics is four 45–minute periods a week.

The Folkeskole Mathematics Syllabus

The curriculum for the Folkeskole is presented in a relatively brief (35 pages) form. The general objectives for mathematics education are set out and these are followed by more specific advice on arithmetic, algebra, geometry, and statistics and probability. There is then a discussion of pedagogical matters. Content, divided into "key-stage" blocks, takes up less than three pages of the document.

Grades 2–3 (ages 7–9)

The natural numbers, zero, ordinals and cardinals, numerals, place system, addition and subtraction, multiplication and division in day-to-day contexts. Elementary geometry, recognition of standard shapes and solids (triangle, rectangle, circle, sphere, cone, etc), language of position (above-below, inside-outside,...), introduction to the concepts of length, area, volume.

Grades 4–6 (ages 9–12)

Further work on naturals, division with remainder. Elementary fractions and simple examples involving addition and subtraction. Decimals and the four operations. Negative numbers (initial informal approach). Simple "commercial" arithmetic. Concept of function and elementary work on sets. Angles, parallels, perpendiculars, symmetry, similarity and congruence, length, area, perimeter and angle measure, capacity. Preparatory work on combinatorics and statistics.

Grades 7–8 (ages 12–14)

Calculating with negative numbers, rationals, powers with positive whole exponents, scientific notation (positive indices). Percentages with applications, use of diagrams and tables. Formation and solution of linear equations in one unknown. Cartesian coordinate system and use of coordinates. Further work on mensuration, angle sum of triangle and angle measure in regular polygons. Experimental work on probability, elementary data handling.

Grades 9–10 (ages 14–16)

Basic course

Rationals and operations, problems requiring rationals for their solution, idea of reals, special square and cube roots, social arithmetic including area and volume. Functions in practical situations and problems, different graphical illustrations.

Geometrical constructions (ruler and compass) and simple properties of figures, Pythagoras and converse. Simple examples on probability.

Advanced course

A deeper understanding of work on number, social arithmetic and mensuration. Functions, graphs and sets (union and intersection), direct and inverse proportionality, linear functions and non-linear functions, eg exponential function, solution of equations and inequalities. Geometrical constructions, introduction to the deductive method, Pythagoras and its converse, applications to coordinate geometry. Collection and displaying of data, grouping, frequencies, elementary work on probability.

Grade 11 (age 16-17)

This is the "extra" year of Folkeskole education and many students will have already left to commence studies in a gymnasium. Mathematics is no longer a compulsory subject. However, it is still offered at two levels. The basic course introduces no new topics. Rather, it concentrates on revising and reinforcing previously introduced material by considering applications and problems arising in a variety of day-to-day situations at work or elsewhere. The advanced course includes additional work on functions, linear equations and inequalities, quadratic functions, equations and inequalities, statistics (median and quartiles) and the combination of probabilities.

The Gymnasium

The Danish Gymnasium is divided into two streams: Languages and Mathematics. In the former, mathematics is not a compulsory subject per se. However, 3 periods a week (each of 45 minutes) in Grade 11 and 4 in Grade 12 are devoted to the Physical Sciences and this course includes some mathematics. In the final Grade (13), mathematics can be taken as an option (4 periods per week).

Within the "mathematics" stream, mathematics is compulsory (5 periods a week) for two years, and is then optional (5 periods a week) in the final year. A final external examination (comprising both an oral and a written examination) can be taken at two levels: B (lower) or A (higher). About three-quarters of students, some 20% of the age cohort, go on to "A" level work.

The syllabuses were revised in 1988. Emphasis was then placed on:
(a) historical, social and cultural aspects,

(b) models and modelling,
(c) mathematics' internal structure and mathematical modes of thought.

The use of the micro is assumed, for example, in connection with the differential and integral calculus, as well as in the "A" level computer mathematics module.

The curricula for the gymnasium are presented in a similar form to those for the Folkeskole, ie very few details are prescribed. The Danish syllabuses, therefore, resemble those of the Netherlands, rather than of, say, Spain or North Rhine Westphalia. However, more detailed guidance is provided in a handbook of directions for teachers.

Abbreviated syllabuses for the two levels are as follows:

B–level

1. **Numbers:** extension of the number concept; rationals, decimals, reals; roots and powers; percentage calculations; time–value–money analysis.

2. **Geometry:** triangles (right–angled and other), trigonometry (sine and cosine rules); analytic description of line and circle (in the plane).

3. **Functions:** linear, polynomial and rational functions; simple trigonometric functions (but not including addition formulae); exponential, power and logarithmic functions; simple equations and inequalities.

4. **Differential calculus:** derivatives and rules for differentiation, maxima and minima, graph sketching; interpretation of derivative (eg slope of tangent, rate of growth); numerical solution of equations (eg Newton–Raphson).

5. **Statistics and probability:** stochastic experiments; concept of probability (a priori, frequential); stochastic variable; binomial and normal distributions.

There is an obligatory written examination (4 hours) for all students at the end of this course. There is also the possibility for students not continuing to A–level to have an oral examination (about 25 minutes in length).

A–level

As above, with the addition of:

6. **Integral calculus and differential equations:** concept of integrability; methods of integration (including numerical, by substitution and by parts); interpretation of integration; differential equations as mathematical models; solution of differential equations (e.g. $y' = ky$, $y'' = ky$, $y' = f(x)g(y)$, $y' = y(b-ay)$).

7. **Vectors in two and three dimensions – geometry:** concept of a vector and vector algebra (with and without co–ordinates); vector projection; analytic description of line, plane, sphere; parametric representation.

8. **Optional topic (about 20 lessons) from within the field of computer mathematics:** ie mathematical topics emphasising the use of algorithmic methods and micros, such as linear programming, chaos, fractals, Computer Assisted Design.

9. **Optional module (25 lessons):** a topic intended to develop the students' ability to undertake further mathematical studies, eg complex numbers, differential equations.

A four–hour written examination for all students is taken after A–level and there is provision for a thirty–minute oral examination. (Such students will have already taken the B–level examination at the end of Grade 12.)

The "Language line" has its own, optional mathematics syllabus. There is little in the way of explicit content. Emphasis is laid on the need for students to learn to formulate, analyse and solve problems making use of their elementary mathematics. In terms of topics, emphasis is laid on functions and optimisation, the representation and analysis of data, and geometry (including consideration of its history and mathematical importance).

FRANCE

<table>
<tr><th>Age (yr)</th><th>Grade</th><th colspan="2"></th></tr>
<tr><td>5-6</td><td>K</td><td colspan="2">Pre-school Education</td></tr>
<tr><td>6-7</td><td>1</td><td colspan="2" rowspan="5">Elementary (Primary) School</td></tr>
<tr><td>7-8</td><td>2</td></tr>
<tr><td>8-9</td><td>3</td></tr>
<tr><td>9-10</td><td>4</td></tr>
<tr><td>10-11</td><td>5</td></tr>
<tr><td>11-12</td><td>6</td><td colspan="2" rowspan="2">Secondary Education</td></tr>
<tr><td>12-13</td><td>7</td></tr>
<tr><td>13-14</td><td>8</td><td rowspan="2">1st cycle</td><td rowspan="3">Technical and Vocational Schools</td></tr>
<tr><td>14-15</td><td>9</td></tr>
<tr><td>15-16</td><td>10</td><td></td></tr>
<tr><td>16-17</td><td>11</td><td rowspan="2">2nd cycle</td><td rowspan="2"></td></tr>
<tr><td>17-18</td><td>12</td></tr>
</table>

Notes

1. Pre-school education is particularly well-developed in France. Free provision is made from the age of 2 and from 3 onwards almost all children participate.

2. Pupils follow a common curriculum until the age of 13 when about 18% opt for vocational courses. By about 1993, the common course will be followed until the age of 15.

3. The main 'academic' stream leads to the Baccalauréat examination at the end of the second cycle of secondary education. However, a variety of Certificates and Brevets are also provided, as are a Baccalauréat professionel and a Baccalauréat technologique.

FRANCE

For many years, France had the reputation of being a country in which, say, 7th grade students throughout the land all had their textbooks open at exactly the same page at any given time. More recently, it was the country associated with some of the worst excesses of modern mathematics in the classroom. The former view is now accepted as a caricature – perhaps it was once related to fact, but it is so no longer. The influences of Bourbaki have also been swept away.

The distinguishing features of French education would now appear to be the comprehensive form which it takes up to the age of 13 (soon 15), and the range of academic, technical and professional streams which then follows. Its traditional form is to be found not in France, but in some of the educationally less developed EC countries which were modelled on the early 20th century French system.

Pre–school education, l'école maternelle, has a long and distinguished history – as early as 1801 there was an institution in Paris for the young children of working mothers, the term 'écoles maternelles' was used by 1848, and the schools were formally established by the 1880s (the decade which saw compulsory, but not free, elementary education established in England). The objectives of such schools are not, of course, framed in mathematical terms but the emphasis on learning to become a 'scholar' and to appreciate that the school and the family have complementary roles is an important one. The activities in which the children engage – physical, those of communication (oral and written), artistic, aesthetic, scientific and technical – all have a bearing upon mathematics education. In particular, within the range of guided scientific and technical activities the child is expected to develop a first understanding of number, classification, and spatial relationships. Most importantly, teachers are trained and pre–school teaching is viewed as a proper vocation.

At present the primary school consists of five classes: the preparatory class (Grade 1), the elementary classes (Grades 2 and 3) and the 'middle' classes (Grades 4 and 5). A fixed national curriculum is laid down for each class: mathematics occupying 6 hours of a 27–hour week. The formal syllabus for mathematics in these years is a very spare one, and is given for the three 'stages' rather than the five grades. The syllabus begins with a clear statement that mathematics demands rigour of thought and clarity of expression – a statement which not only reinforces stereotyped views of the French, but also will cheer many mathematicians elsewhere. Some short remarks on pedagogy include a brief look at the different roles of problems in prompting mathematical activities. The syllabuses then follow (we give an abridged version). The 'meaning' of the syllabus can only be supplied by examples of 'practice' in the form of texts, advice from subject associations, etc.

Preparatory class (Grade 1, age 6–7)

Arithmetic: classification and arrangement of objects by simple or compound criteria. Numerals up to 100, discovery of numbers beyond 100, distinction between ordinal and cardinal numbers, comparison of two numbers (equal, less than, greater than – symbols), increasing and decreasing sequences of numbers, addition and problems requiring sum of two or more numbers, use of brackets, construction, use and memorisation of addition table, problems of the form (numbers not letters) a + .. = c, mental arithmetic.

Geometry: positioning in space (objects in relation to oneself), using grids, diagrams and regions, interior and exterior, rosettes, friezes, pavings, mosaics, puzzles.

Preparatory work on measure: ordering events in the day and the week, classifying and ordering objects by length and weight.

Elementary classes (Grades 2 and 3, ages 7–9)

Arithmetic: numerals and names of natural numbers, revision of equality and inequality symbols, problems leading to addition, subtraction and multiplication, expression of a number in different written forms, use of operation properties, mental arithmetic, use of brackets, construction, use and memorisation of multiplication tables, encountering problems necessitating division, determination of quotient by an empirical method, order of size and context of a result, the notion of addition of a and multiplication by a as unary operations on the naturals and problems related to these.

Geometry: Position of nodes of a grid, reproduction, description, representation and construction of solids, surfaces and lines making use of usual instruments, various types of paper, etc, development of a geometrical vocabulary, first notions of symmetry, translations.

Quantities and measure: events through the day, week, month, year, duration (verbal and symbolical), metric units of length and mass.

Middle classes (Grades 4 and 5, ages 9–11)

Arithmetic: necessity for new numbers, decimal fractions, simple vulgar fractions, problems requiring the four operations on decimals, comparison of decimals, proportionality, mental arithmetic with decimals.

Geometry: further work as in previous grades, distance, enlargements and reductions using squared paper, drawing parallels and perpendiculars, further vocabulary: cube, edge, vertex, face, sphere, ball, circle, disc (note dimensional distinctions), triangle, quadrilateral, parallelogram, rectangle, rhombus, square, side, diagonal.

Quantities and measure: formation of concepts of length, area, volume, mass, angle and duration, use of systems of measure (metric and common), calculations involving length and weights, use of measuring instruments, determination of the circumference of a circle, areas of a disc, a rectangle and a triangle, volume of a cuboid, use of formulae for area and volume.

Some important changes are now planned for the organization of primary schools. Three fundamental 'cycles' are envisaged –

ages 2–5 :	'cycle des premiers apprentissages',
ages 5–8 :	'cycle des apprentissages fondamentaux',
ages 8–11:	'cycle des approfondissements'.

In general, each cycle is 3 years long; some pupils, however, will cover the work in 2 years, others in 4. No major changes to the content printed above are envisaged.

Lower Secondary Education

The syllabuses for Grades 6–9 (Classes 6–3 in the French style) date from 1989 and are of special interest. They result from close collaboration between various groups involved in mathematics education and display an interesting blend of prescription and freedom.

The work begins with a statement of the principal aims for that stage of education which include the acquisition of the culture necessary for life, work and citizenship. More specifically, mathematics teaching is seen to have two aspects: one concerns the way that mathematics is derived from and met in many disciplines, the other the way that, in return, mathematical knowledge and methods can contribute to various specialities. In a manner which hints at 'old–fashioned' faculty psychology but which, nevertheless, must still have some justification, it is pointed out that mathematics education should assist the intellectual development of the pupil through:

developing reasoning powers: observation, analysis, deductive thought;
stimulating the imagination;
promoting the habit of clear expression, both written and oral;
stressing the qualities of proceeding methodically and with care.

In setting out the syllabus a distinction is drawn between: prescribed activities which should be as rich and diverse as possible, expected knowledge which will be much less than that mathematics touched upon in class, and possible complementary activities.

A section on general pedagogy precedes the programme proper. This begins by stressing the need constantly to consolidate material taught previously and, for example, to make use of the pocket calculator, and, where appropriate, the micro.

The work for each year is then given in summary form and this is followed by explanatory notes for teachers. There is a standard allowance of time for the teaching of mathematics: 3 hours per week in Grades 6 and 7 (plus frequently one additional hour for remedial work), 4 hours per week in Grades 8 and 9. Limited use is made of having a weak student repeat a year.

A summary table for the four years is included and it is this (with some additional notes) which forms the basis for what follows.

Grade 6 (age 11–12)

Measures and quantities: perimeter and area of square and rectangle, circumference of circle, volume of cuboid, common units of length, area, volume, angle measure, (the use of 'letters' in algebra is presaged through the use of formulae for area and volumes)

Position, distance and angles (continued in Grade 7): position of a point on a line (introduction of negative numbers), on a grid (coordinates)

Figures, constructions, transformations: cuboid, rectangle, rhombus, triangle, isosceles triangle, circle, line symmetry (conservation of distances, collinearity, angles, area), constructions of axes of symmetry (mediator, bisectors,...)

Numbers: naturals and decimals, truncating and rounding off, orders of size, divisibility criteria (2, 3, 5, 9), decimals written as fractions, quotient of two decimals (using calculator), ordering of numbers, simple equations (with frames)

Representation and organisation of data (continued in Grade 7): tables and graphs (bar, line and pie charts in Grade 7)

Numerical functions: multiplication by a fraction $^a/_b$, percentage and (continued in Grade 7) the effect on length, area and volume of changes in units of measure, changes of scale on a map, proportionality.

Grade 7 (age 12–13) – see also topics carried over from Grade 6

Measures and quantities: areas of parallelogram, triangle, disc (circle), surface area and volume of cylinder, right prisms, angle sum, units of time

Figures, constructions, transformations: right prisms, cylinders, parallelograms (construction and characterisation), concurrency of mediators of triangle, point symmetry (invariants, applications), circumscribed circle of triangle

Numbers and algebra: comparison and addition of fractions with same denominator, multiplication of fractions, $k(a+b) = ka + kb$, comparison, addition and subtraction of decimals (including negative numbers), $a + x = b$, $ax = b$ (use of letters in equations)

Numerical functions: average speed, percentage, proportionality, use of area and volume formulae.

Grade 8 (age 13–14)

Measure and quantities: area of sphere, volume of ball, and (continued in Grade 9) quotients and products of units (km/h , m/s , passenger km, kwh)

Position, distance and angles: triangle inequality, distance of a point from a line, cosine as an operator (perpendicular projection), Pythagoras and converse, slope of a line

Figures, constructions and transformations: sphere, plane sections, projection in a given direction, conservation of mid-points, concurrency of bisectors, medians, altitudes in a triangle, circumscribed circle of a right-angled triangle, transformation of figures by translation and rotation, regular polygons.

Numbers and algebra: the four operations on decimals and fractions (positive and negative), effect of addition and multiplication on order, integer exponents, standard (scientific) notation, expanding $(a+b)(c+d)$, use of literal expressions ('with prudence'!), linear equations and inequalities in one unknown and applications.

Representation and organisation of data: frequencies, as a percentage, cumulative frequencies.

Numerical functions: proportionality, mappings, percentages, indices.

Grade 9 (ages 14–15)

Measures and quantities: volumes of a pyramid and cone of revolution, effects of enlargement and reduction on length, area, volume, mass.

Position, distance, angles: coordinates of a vector in the plane, vector addition, trigonometry of the right–angled triangle, distance between two points, $y = mx + c$

Figures, constructions, transformations: pyramids, cones of revolution, sections by planes parallel to the base, angle at centre of circle is twice ..., Thales for triangle, composition of two translations, two point symmetries, two reflections in parallel or perpendicular lines.

Numbers and algebra: factorisation of a^2-b^2, $a^2+2ab+b^2$, $a^2-2ab+b^2$, simple calculations with square roots, two simultaneous linear equations in two unknowns with applications, $(ax+b)(cx+d) = 0 \Longrightarrow \ldots$, algebraic and graphical solutions.

Representation and organisation of data: mean, mean of grouped data, median.

Numerical functions: affine maps (using graphs), proportionality (including examples with products and quotients of units), analysis and construction of algorithms.

The Upper Secondary School (2nd cycle; 15–18 years)

This stage of education is divided into three streams: general, technological and professional. The last, which can end at 16 or 17, is extremely diverse (several hundred different diplomas) and pays little attention to mathematics. The numbers taking the general and technological streams are in the rough ratio of 7 to 1. However, the ratios for the successful completion of the baccalauréat are nearer 2 to 1. Again, these two streams have many subdivisions (and even smaller parts, for the F stream has 12 tributaries!). The following table offers a simplified description and also indicates the number of hours devoted to mathematics per week in each section. (A week is 26–28 hours in general education, over 30 in technical.)

Grade 10		**Grade 11**		**Grade 12**	
		A1 Arts–Maths	5	A1	5
		A2 Arts–Lang.	2	A2	2
		A3 Arts–arts	2	A3	2
General	4 hrs	B Economics	5	B	5
		S Sciences	6	C Maths–Phys	9
				D Maths Biol	6
		G Management	1½	G1 Secretarial	0
		Accounting	3½	G2 Accounting	3½
Technical	3 hrs			G3 Marketing	2½
		E Maths–Tech.	6	E	9
		F Industrial or Lab.Technology	3–5	F	2–5

The demands made by the much–esteemed Section C acted as a deterrent to recruitment to higher education in mathematics and physics (although many who take this Section do not go on to study these subjects at university). The numbers taking it grew very slowly: 30400 in 1975, 34500 in 1986 out of a total, by then, of some 275000 'bacheliers'. As a result, mathematics 2nd–cycle syllabuses were somewhat hurriedly revised in the mid–1980s: practical work was made obligatory, and the amount of theory reduced (limits, series, linear algebra, geometric transformations).

As examples of the syllabuses available we outline below those for Sections C and E and also those for Sections A1 and B.

Grade 10 (ages 15–16 years) – applicable to all students

Numerical activities (preparatory to study of functions and to aid cross–curricular activities); operations and inequalities on real numbers (emphasis on decimals and rationals), absolute value, distance, examples of approximations to reals, use of bounds, intervals, statistical descriptions, tables of data, survey responses, ..., various graphical representations, class size, frequency, cumulative frequency, means.

Functions: graphical representation, odd and even, periodicity, increasing, decreasing, maximum, minimum, $ax + b$, $|x|$, x^2, x^3, $\sqrt{x}$, $1/x$, behaviour for large values of x, trig functions, trigonometrical circle, relations ($\cos(x+\pi) = ...$) (**no** addition formulae expected).

Plane geometry: homotheties (dilations), link with scalar multiplication of vectors, effect on lengths and areas, images of lines and circles, barycentre of two, three or four weighted points, parametric equation of straight line, circle, tangents, symmetries, convexity of disc, equation of circle.

3-D geometry: incidence, parallelism, orthogonality, projections, orthogonal projections, cartesian coordinates, calculation of lengths, areas and volumes.

Scalar product in the plane: definition, formula, characterisation of orthogonality, symmetry, linearity, orthonormal basis, norm, distance between points in an orthonormal system, $\mathbf{x}.\mathbf{n} = 0$ as a line.

Systems of linear equations: two linear equations or inequalities in two unknowns, solution by substitution and graphically.

Grade 11 (16–17)

Sections A1 and B (5 hours per week)

Statistics: representation of data–tree, double entry table, partitions, use of set language for describing classification, quantitative and qualitative variables, mean and quartiles, practical activities.

Numerical and algebraic activities: factorisation by $x - a$, quadratics, graphical solution of a system of equations or inequalities in two unknowns, algebraic solution of linear systems, bounds and intervals, precision, scientific notation, order of x, x^2, x^3, $\sqrt{x}$ when $x \geq 1$ and $0 \leq x \leq 1$.

Numerical sequences and functions: generating sequences, $f(x)$, recursive definitions, APs and GPs, increasing and decreasing sequences, the language of limits, practical examples (interest, biological and other growth), sum, product, composition of functions, $f \geq g$, $f \geq 0$, functions in the neighbourhood of the origin, limits, derivative at a point, on an interval, derived function, properties of derived function ($f' = 0 \Rightarrow \ldots$, $f' > 0 \Longrightarrow$ etc), $f + \lambda$, λf, $f(x+\lambda)$, $f(\lambda x)$, maxima and minima, graphs, exponential function (and applications).

Plane geometry: examples on distances, area, angles, triangles, regular polygons, use of geometrical techniques in surveying, geography, architecture,...

Sections S and E (6 hours per week)

Statistics: frequencies, cumulative frequencies, histograms, mean and quartiles (introduction of sigma notation)

Numerical and algebraic problems: factorisation by $(x-a)$, canonical form of quadratic, sum and product of roots, graphical solution of equations in two unknowns, systems of linear equations, bounds and intervals, etc. (as in A1 and B)

Numerical sequences As A1 and B but with a stronger emphasis on rigour (eg 'if one establishes that $|u_n - L| \leq \lambda\alpha_n$ where α_n tends to zero, then u_n tends to L'.), examples of the use of sequences in approximations to a number ($\sqrt{2}$, area of disc,...)

Numerical functions: as A1 and B with more rigorous treatment of limit of $g(h)$ as h tends to zero, approximation to a function at a point by an affine function (ie approximating curve by a straight line), $f(a+h) = f(a) + Ah + h\phi(h)$ where $\phi(h) \to 0$ as $h \to 0$, derivative at a point, tangent, speed, $(f(a+h) - f(a))/h$, derivatives of sum, product, inverse, quotient, of $f(ax+b)$, $\sqrt{x}$, theorems on differentiable functions, circular functions, graphs, maxima and minima.

Geometry: points, vectors and position in the plane and in space, collinearity, parallelism of lines, bases, coplanar vectors, parallelism of two planes, of a line and a plane, scalar product in space, orthogonality of two lines, line and a plane, normal vector, perpendicular planes, orthogonal projection, orthonormal bases, norm, distance, angles in the plane, orientation, rotations of the plane, addition formulae for cosine and sine, plane sections of prisms, pyramids, sphere, distances and areas, sine and cosine rules for triangle, $x^2 + y^2 = k$, $x^2 - y^2 = k$, and $xy = k$.

Transformations and configurations in the plane: the effect of translations, reflections, rotations and homotheties on parallelism, equipollency, barycentres, distances, angles and areas, isometries, composition of rotations and reflections, decomposition, isometries leaving figures invariant, interchanging two lines, etc.

Grade 12 (ages 17–18)

Sections A1 and B (5 hours per week)

Emphasis is put on the use of a programmable scientific calculator (for use with recurrence relations, etc.)

Complex Numbers (Only A1 and included essentially for cultural reasons): complex numbers, conjugates, geometric representation, modulus, triangle inequality, solution of quadratics

Statistics (only B): bivariate distributions, tables, marginal frequencies, conditional frequencies, least squares, lines of regression, coefficient of linear correlation

Combinatorics and probability: cardinality of $A \times B$, A^p , permutations, combinations, ^nCr and elementary relations, binomial theorem, events, elementary events, definition of probability, disjoint events, union and intersection, conditional probability, independence, successive trials, Bernoulli, binomial distribution, practical work

Analysis: chain rule, second and higher derivatives, inequalities and differentiability (eg if $m \leq f' \leq M$ and $a < b$ then $m(b-a) \leq ...$) primitives, limits as $x \rightarrow +\infty$ and $x \rightarrow -\infty$, comparison of functions and of their limits, limits of sum, product, quotient and composed functions, logarithmic and exponential functions, differentiation, asymptotic behaviour, e , powers, comparison of growth, graphs, approximations, applications, growth and decay

The integral calculus: primitives, definite integrals, linearity (Chasles), integration of an inequality (if $m \leq f \leq M$ and $a \leq b$ then $m(b-a) \leq ...$), primitives of $g'(ax+b)$ and g'/g (ie limited substitution), integration by parts, areas, volumes of usual solids (ball, prism, ...)

Geometry: centred on two principal objectives - maintaining and supporting previous work in 2- and 3-D, exploiting geometry as a source of problems and maintaining a geometric vision through systematic graphical activities.

Sections C and E (9 hours per week)

Combinatorics and probability: as A1 and B but omitting conditional probability, independence, Bernoulli and binomial distribution and including inclusion and exclusion formula and Binomial theorem on $\mathbb{C}$.

Complex numbers: as A1 plus argument, de Moivre, formulae for sine and cosine, $a \cos \theta + b \sin \theta$, trigonometric product formulae, n^{th} roots of unity, geometric interpretation

Systems of linear equations: solution by elementary operations (Gauss), geometrical interpretations

Numerical sequences: global behaviour, increasing, decreasing, monotonic, bounded, periodic, usual properties of limits (no proofs), operations on limits, properties of bounded, monotonic sequences, use of sequences when approximating to a number

Numerical functions: introduction of general limit notation (in addition to $x \to 0$), continuity and differentiability, usual properties of limits (no proofs), chain rule, higher derivatives, inequalities on finite intervals, primitives of a continuous function, logarithmic, exponential and power functions, sin, cos, tan, comparison of reference functions, behaviour for large (and small) x, numerical solutions of equations.

Integral calculus: primitives, definite integral, linearity (Chasles), inequality of the mean, mean value of a function, techniques (as A1 and B), linear differential equations with constant coefficients of first order or of second order with no first order term, applications to areas, volumes, growth, decay, etc.

Geometry: barycentres, vector characterisation of segment, half–line, line, plane, linearity of a vectorial projection, conservation of barycentres, orthonormal basis, vector product, analytic expression in directed orthonormal basis, determinant of two vectors ($\det(\mathbf{a}, \mathbf{b}) = ab \sin \theta$), collinearity of vectors, distances of point from a line in the plane, from a line and a plane in space, analytic description of a translation, and a rotation in the plane

Curves in the plane: parametric definition, $x(t)\mathbf{i} + y(t)\mathbf{j}$, derived vector, interpretation, tangent, conics, focus and directrix properties, eccentricity, parabola, central conic, $y^2 = 2ax$, $ax^2 + by^2 = c$, $(a \cos t, b \sin t)$, plane isometries, composition, inverse, decomposition, invariants, linearity, characterisation of displacements, direct similarities, composition of dilation and rotation with the same centre, effect on distances and angles, composition of direct similarities, reduced form, given A, B $(A \neq B)$ and A', B' $(A' \neq B')$ there exists a direct similarity such that $A \to A'$, $B \to B'$, vector transformation associated with a direct similarity, compatibility of composition, notions of elementary transformations in 3–D, translation, homothety, central symmetry, reflection (in a plane), rotation defined by axis and angle, half–turn, decomposition of a rotation as a product of two reflections.

Grades 11 and 12: Section A2 and A3

This 2 hours a week course at present concentrates on statistics, (representation, mean, quartiles), sequences (as in A1), differentiation (x^n, $\sqrt{x}$), simple probability (drawing from urns, dice,...), functions (behaviour for large x, exponential function). Options are offered in numbers ($\mathbb{C}$), statistics (bivariate distribution), geometry (symmetry of figures, regular polygons and π, remarkable curves), probability (successive events, binomial distribution, history of probability) and astronomy (time, celestial mechanics).

At present the replacement of this course by one on the history of mathematics and science is under consideration.

GERMANY

(The diagram describes the system of what was Federal Germany)

Age (yr)	Grade			
5-6	K	Pre-school		
6-7	1	Elementary (Grundschule)		
7-8	2			
8-9	3			
9-10	4			
10-11	5	Gymnasium	Realschule	Hauptschule
11-12	6			
12-13	7			
13-14	8			
14-15	9			
15-16	10			
16-17	11			
17-18	12			
18-19	13			

Notes

1. Pre-school education in the Federal Republic was largely (80%) state-funded, but independently organised. It was not seen as part of the educational system.

2. The pattern shown above has many variations. In particular, Grades 5-6 are often seen as 'orientation' years and as a prolongation of the common Grundschule. Comprehensive schools, encompassing Grades 5-10, exist in some Länder.

3. Although the age for compulsory school attendance is 15, it is now becoming common to include a 10th Grade Hauptschule course.

GERMANY

As mentioned in the Introduction, this account was prepared before the unification of Germany. As a result, it describes the system which existed in the Federal Republic. The system in the German Democratic Republic was very different. That was a comprehensive system with a single mathematics curriculum and one, state-provided series of textbooks. One result of unification is almost certain to be an increase in educational diversity within what was East Germany. In particular, patterns which are described below will probably be adopted. What follows, then, is still likely to provide an appropriate guide to mathematics education within the new Germany.

The German system, like those of the Netherlands, Austria and Switzerland, is still largely characterised by its degree of differentiation through school types. The word 'largely' is needed here for, in practice, there is no one West German educational system: each of the eleven Länder (Baden-Württemberg, Bayern (Bavaria), Berlin, Bremen, Hamburg, Hessen, Niedersachsen, Nordrhein-Westfalen, Rheinland-Pfalz, Saarland and Schleswig-Holstein) has its own mini-system, and its own curricula. In some Länder the 'comprehensive' *Gesamtschule* occupies a significant position within the system. In general, though, it is still most apt to think of the West German secondary school system comprising three types of school: the *Gymnasium* which has a fundamentally academic character and prepares students for university, the *Realschule* which has a more technical bias, and the *Hauptschule* which provides general basic education up to the age of 15. Nationally, students divide between these three types of school in roughly equal proportions.

The result of these many divisions is that one cannot speak of a German "national curriculum". Indeed, in 1986 the Institut für Didaktik der Mathematik, Bielefeld issued a book of over two hundred pages merely giving bibliographic details of the various *Mathematik-Lehrpläne* (800 or so!) to be found within the Federal Republic. (These do, however, cover much of what we in England would refer to as Further (or Technical/Commercial) Education.)

Here then we must be necessarily selective. Below we shall give details of curricula from two Länder: the 'conservative', prosperous Baden-Württemberg and the somewhat more progressive, more densely populated Nordrhein-Westfalen.

Just as the curricula differ from Land to Land, so do examination practices. The **Abitur** was established in 18th century Prussia and is the precursor of all university entrance examinations. From its beginning it was essentially directed by teachers and, particularly in the central and northern Länder, it remains so. There was also a tradition of certification after the 10th grade and this is now carried on through the 'Mittlere Reife' and 'Abschlussprüfung' qualifications. Again, whilst these are more formally administered and controlled in the two southernmost Länder, elsewhere they are largely directed by schools and teachers. At the end of every year there is school-based, teacher-assessed certification: and successful completion of the 10th grade provides the 'Mittlere Reife' qualification.

Promotion at the end of the year is by no means automatic in German schools. The ages given below alongside the classes assume regular promotion.

Pre-school education took a markedly different form in Federal Germany from that in most other countries. It is relatively well-established, about 40% of all 3-year olds attend some form of institution and it is largely (80%) publicly financed. However, it is not seen as part of the formal educational system; there is no official curriculum and it is independently organised.

Baden-Württemberg

Grundschule (Primary/Elementary School, ages 6-10)

The curriculum for the primary school is introduced by a general discussion of aims and methods of working. Thus, for example, advice is given on the setting of homework tasks, the relation between play and learning, the need to cater for children of different abilities and attainments through individual, partner and group work, the need for practice and revision, etc., and also on cooperation with parents and teacher-training institutions. This is followed by chapters on individual subjects within the curriculum. Here again the detailed curriculum is preceded by a general discussion of goals. For example, it is pointed out that arithmetic is the central component of each of the four years' study, and that in geometry emphasis must be put on activities: drawing, folding, cutting, sticking, measuring, etc.

Mathematics is given its own time allocation, 4 hours (for 30 weeks) in Grade 1 and 5 hours per week in Grades 2-4. Within each year recommendations are made for the number of hours (in total, not in one block) to be devoted to the four themes: arithmetic, magnitude, practical applications, and geometry. Content is presented by providing 'broad' headings, together with explanatory remarks and examples. In some cases unequivocal guidance is provided on how certain algorithms are to be set out (eg subtraction and long multiplication) and the way in which the child is to form numerals when writing.

Grade 1 (6–7) (We provide an edited version of the 'broad' description of content)

1. Acquisition of basic experiences (20 hours)

Properties of objects in the child's environment (eg sorting toys by colour, form and type); relations between objects (eg differences between objects); relationships of position (right, left, before, behind, etc).

2. Arithmetic (50 hours)

Reading and writing numbers up to 20; multiples of 10 up to 100; equality and ordering (including use of <, =, >), counting forwards and backwards; addition and subtraction, zero, doubling and halving; number sequences; examples on 'neighbours', exchanges and analogues (eg 15+4 = 19, 14+4 = .., 4+15 = .., 5+4 = ..).

3. Magnitude and quantities (10 hours)

Coins and banknotes.

4. Practical exercises (30 hours)

Mathematics drawn from daily life and play; simple reckoning; oral examples on buying, selling, saving, lending, ...; simple written examples.

5. Geometry (10 hours)

Building with different materials; examples of basic shapes drawn from the child's environment (squares, triangles, circles).

Grade 2 (7–8)

1. Arithmetic (60 hours)

Numbers to 100, reading and writing numerals, decomposition using properties (swimmers, non–swimmers, etc.), equality, successors and predecessors, doubling and halving, ordering, addition and subtraction (revision and extension), simple equations with one place–holder (eg 36+.. = 59), greater than and less than, multiplication (repeated addition and combinatoric situations (2 boys and 3 girls – how many pairs possible?)), 2, 4, 5, 10 and 3 times tables, division (various aspects: separation into equal parts, reversing multiplication, repeated subtraction), representation of operations by arrow diagrams and tables.

2. Magnitude and quantities (30 hours)

Coins and notes up to 100DM (more than, less than); lengths, non-conventional units and then m , cm , phrases for comparison; time, non-conventional units leading to second, minute,..., month, year; reading a clock (eg twenty three minutes past five).

3. Practical exercises (45 hours)

Using mathematics in a variety of day-to-day activities; simple graphical representation (birthdays, hobbies), situations involving counting and calculating.

4. Geometry (15 hours)

Looking at day-to-day shapes, drawing freehand and with stencils, discovering and making line symmetric figures, drawing and displaying patterns and figures, using squared and other paper, comparing shapes.

Grade 3 (8-9)

1. Arithmetic (50 hours)

Numbers to 1000, revision of reading and writing numbers, relating multiplication tables to practical situations, relations between numbers (half of, has a larger tens digit than,...), ordering natural numbers in ascending or descending order, addition and subtraction (using given algorithms), tables up to 10×10, multiplication and division (two digit numbers multiplied or divided by one digit numbers, with remainders where appropriate), simple multiples and divisors, simple equations to be solved by a systematic trial-and-improvement approach.

2. Magnitude and quantities (30 hours)

Banknotes and coins, standard form for writing amounts in DM and Pf; lengths, km, m, dm, cm (standard form for lengths); weights, comparison, heavier than, self-chosen units leading to standard g, kg, t (tonne); capacity, litre (half and quarter); time (revision, extension, eg use of stopwatch).

3. Practical exercises (40 hours)

Using the four operations on day-to-day examples, constructing tables, using units of money, length, weight, volume, time.

4. Geometry (30 hours)

Standard solids eg cube, sphere, cylinder; standard shapes, triangle, rectangle, square, circle, drawing and measuring, areas of very simple shapes such as squares and some triangles, further work on symmetry including drawings on squared paper, introduction to specifying position of points on squared paper.

Class 4 (9–10)

1. Arithmetic (40 hours)

Numbers to one million, place value, simple sequences, relations between numbers (10 times, 100 times), rounding to nearest ten, hundred, thousand, emphasis on reckoning with powers of tens and their multiples, order of operations and breaking down operations into steps ($7 \times 56 = 7 \times 50 + 7 \times 6$), equations with one place–holder, adding (three or more numbers) and subtraction, long multiplication with up to three digit numbers, long division by numbers up to 20 (all operations to be set out in a standard, given form), simple estimates, properties of numbers, divisors and multiples.

2. Magnitude and quantities (30 hours)

Revision and extensions eg use of timetables, use of decimal point when giving weights.

3. Practical exercises (50 hours)

Applying the mathematics learned to problems in everyday life, hobbies, sport etc. with special attention paid to tables, diagrams, timetables, etc., use of automatic weighing machines, calculating dates of school holidays, etc.

4. Geometry (30 hours)

Solids and shapes (construction using paper, straws, wood etc.), nets of simple shapes (eg cubes), building solids using unit cubes; drawing and measuring, the right angle (set square), drawing parallel lines (and recognising them in everyday contexts), drawing simple shapes (different quadrilaterals, right–angled triangles), areas of figures drawn on squared paper (including dealing with half squares).

The Hauptschule

The Hauptschule covers classes 5–9 (ie up to 15, the school–leaving age). The presentation of the syllabus is preceded by an explanation of the specific aims of the Hauptschule, eg that it is intended as a neighbourhood school, aiming to provide a broad education which will equip students for entry to a number of trades and will prepare them for active citizenship. It is expected that education begun in the Hauptschule will be continued in a two–year Berufsfachschule which prepares its students for a particular vocation. Transfers from the Hauptschule to the Realschule or Gymnasium are possible and, in suitable cases, encouraged. At the end of the Hauptschule, students take a leaving examination (Abschlussprüfung).

The syllabus is presented in the same form as that adopted for other levels in Baden–Württemburg, ie the work for each year is divided into four or so sections and an indication of the time to be devoted to each section is given. Within each section there is a brief paragraph giving overall aims, a list of topics to be covered and a supplementary list of examples of work to be covered.

Note that in each of Grades 5–8, 16 hours are set aside for student assessment.

Grade 5 (10–11)

1. Natural numbers (52 hours)

Revision of basic operations on the naturals (including eg the writing of dictated numbers in numeral form), mental arithmetic, squares (up to 20^2).

2. Basic Geometry (24 hours)

Points, segments, lines; parallel, perpendicular, distance; basic quadrilaterals and solids; faces, edges, vertices; nets; axial symmetry and translations using squared paper.

3. Measuring–estimating–calculating (28 hours)

A selection of practical, everyday examples in this area, including basic work on area (square and rectangle), volume (cuboid), revision of standard units, use of price–tables.

Class 6 (11–12)

1. Divisors of natural numbers (20 hours)

This preparatory work for fractions includes divisors and multiples (use of representations – tree (Hasse) diagrams, arrow diagrams etc.), rules for division (5, 10, 25, 2, 4, 3, 6, 9), primes, lcm, hcf, intersection and union of sets (Venn diagrams).

2. Fractions (36 hours)

Fractions as quantities and as operators (including fractions greater than 1), equivalent fractions, addition and multiplication of fractions, comparison and ordering.

3. Fractions in decimal form (28 hours)

Converting from vulgar to decimal fractions and vice–versa, terminating and recurring decimals, comparison and ordering of decimals.

4. Calculating with quantities (26 hours)

Rounding decimal numbers, estimation, practical examples including eg volume/price, volume/weight, and distance/time.

5. Simple geometrical activities (24 hours)

Work on drawing and modelling, in connection with circle (midpoint, radius, diameter), angles (use of set square), point–reflections, rotations (centre of, angle of) using squared paper, and common solids (models of prism, cylinder, pyramid, cone, sphere).

It is perhaps useful to make the first comparisons with North Rhine–Westphalia (N–W) at this stage. There, Grades 5–6 of the Hauptschule are considered as forming a 'key stage'. Time to be spent on various sections is suggested (eg natural numbers, 14–17 weeks), as is the time to be spent on sub–sections, eg divisors (cf. section 1 of Grade 6 for B–W), about 5 weeks. A rough breakdown of material between the two years is suggested. The N–W syllabus dates from 1977 and this is evident, for example, in the emphasis on fractions as operators which reflects work done in the early '70s by the CSMP group in the US. So far as content is concerned there are some apparent differences in emphasis eg different number bases in N–W, fluency in arithmetical algorithms in B–W. Perhaps the most significant differences are the introduction of descriptive statistics (including mean, relative frequencies and probability) in N–W, and the somewhat deeper treatment of transformation geometry provided there.

Grade 7 (12–13)

(Occasionally optional topics are recommended at this and later grades: we omit references to these)

1. Applied calculations (48 hours)

Revision of decimal and vulgar fractions, percentages (use of eg pie charts and bar graphs for representation, examples on profit, loss, discount), proportion (direct and inverse).

2. Basic constructions, congruence and mensuration (34 hours)

Bisection of line and angle, drawing perpendicular, angle theorems (angle sum for 3– and 4–gons), coordinate systems, congruence, figures with equal area, formulae for areas of square and rectangle, volumes of cuboid and cube.

3. The integers (10 hours)

Negative numbers (via temperature, debits and credits), the number line, ordering, differences (no formal rules, no equations).

4. Equations and inequalities (12 hours)

Solutions through examples of change, systematic trials (no equivalence of statements but working towards identification of a formal approach).

Class 8 (13–14)

1. Applied calculations (44 hours)

Revision of calculations with fractions and percentages; the rule of three; rates (price per litre, pay per hour, density, flow (volume per second)), graphs (reading, drawing, interpreting: examples of direct and inverse proportion, rounding off numbers, seeking extreme values, distance–time diagrams, etc.).

2. Constructions and mensuration (44 hours)

Triangles (SSS, SAS, ASA); quadrilaterals; area (formulae for parallelogram, trapezium, triangle, circle (including $2\pi r$)), surface areas of cylinders and right prisms, sketching solids (oblique projection), volumes of cylinders and right prisms.

3. Integers and rationals (8 hours)

Work on the number line, rules for addition and subtraction.

4. Equations and inequalities (8 hours)

Solution of linear equations and inequalities.

Class 9 (14–15) (N–W)

1. Applied calculations (60 hours)

Use of calculator, fractions, percent, interest, H.P., rates, graphs (pie and bar charts), averages, basic statistics.

2. Various solids, Pythagoras (23 hours)

Constructions (regular n–gons), Pythagoras and applications (no formal, derived proof - only plausibility), pyramids and cones, volume formulae, surface area, representation of 3–D solids, volume of the sphere.

3. Calculations with rational numbers, roots and powers (22 hours)

Revision and extension, square roots, scientific notation.

4. Equations and formula (20 hours)

Equations and change of variables.

As was the case with the syllabuses for Grades 5 and 6, N–W presents its curriculum in two–year key–stages. Perhaps the most important feature of the N–W syllabus for Grades 7 and 8 is that it envisages differentiated mathematics courses *within* the Hauptschule, ie that there will be a basic foundation course offered and, in addition, an extended course. There are some significant differences between the B–W and N–W syllabuses. In particular N–W suggests that calculators are introduced in Grade 7 (it is stressed that the suggested programme is not binding; teachers and schools are free to adopt other teaching sequences), and, again, N–W pays more attention to descriptive statistics (eg mean and median, and the obtaining of statistical data from probabilistic experiments). Comparison between the two syllabuses is made difficult because of the greater detail supplied in N–W and also the more 'modern' language and notation in which the N–W syllabus is couched (which might not necessarily have any effect whatsoever on what is actually taught and learned in classrooms). In general, the emphasis on using arithmetic and on mensuration is shared with B–W. 'Pure' geometry, however, ie descriptions of transformations, and classification in general, would seem to be emphasised more in N–W than B–W within Grades 7 and 8. Differentiation of mathematics courses continues in Grades 9 and 10, partly to reflect the fact that students will be following different paths within the school curriculum as a whole. Because the expectations of 'low–attainers' differ so much from country to country, it is perhaps of value to give the N–W syllabuses for the basic course at this key–stage (ending at age 16 in N–W) in somewhat greater (but far from full) detail.

Class 9 (14–15) (N–W)

1. Numbers and algebra (c.6 weeks)

Powers and roots (using calculator), revision of previous work on fractions, negatives, etc, $(a\pm b)^2$, $(a+b)(a-b)$.

2. Practical calculations (c.14 weeks)

Percentage, interest, mixtures, simple growth processes, common functions and graphs (timetables, temperature, rainfall, examples from commerce and industry), $y = mx+c$.

3. Geometry (c.11 weeks)

Mensuration (including eg formulae for areas of circle sectors, volume of pyramids and cones), nets and surface area of pyramids, drawing solids (oblique projection), Pythagoras and simple applications, Thales, congruence theorems for triangles (unique construction), similarity of figures through enlargements.

Class 10 (15–16) (N–W)

1. Number and algebra (c.10 weeks)

Working with formulae, square roots, standard (scientific) notation, rationals and irrationals, linear equations in two unknowns (including simultaneous equations), quadratic equations ($x^2 = q$ only – general quadratic is in extended course).

2. Practical calculations (c.8 weeks)

Further examples from business and industry (including extended work on particular themes), linear and quadratic functions, graphs and their interpretation.

3. Geometry (c.13 weeks)

Revision and extension of mensuration (eg surface area and volume of sphere), solids of revolution, simple plane sections (introduction to conic sections on the extended course), proof in geometry (eg Pythagoras and Thales). (Trigonometry of the right–angled triangle on the extended course).

Realschule

Grades 5–6 (10–12)

The mathematics syllabus for the Realschule in Baden–Württemberg is not significantly different from that for the Hauptschule. Suggestions for additional work are included (eg other number systems, further examples on constructions using ruler and setsquare, scales in connection with maps) and on occasions (eg calculation with fractions) it is specifically suggested that Realschule students might attempt more complicated work. The same approach is *not* taken in North Rhine–Westphalia. Here there are significant differences between the two syllabuses – that for the Realschule appears to have been constructed by a different working group from that responsible for the Hauptschule and the syllabus and its presentation demonstrate to a far greater extent the 'modern mathematics' influence as represented by, say, Papy. For example, set language and arrows abound. ((E) denotes extension material.)

Grade 5 (N–W)

1. Finite sets

Set, defining statement, element, subset, empty set, intersection, union, complement, difference, cardinality (has more elements than), representation of sets, arrow diagrams, simple probabilistic experiments. (E) relations (transitivity, symmetry, reflexivity), product sets, further experiments, tree diagrams to represent possible happenings.

2. Natural numbers

Decimal and binary systems, 0 and 1 as neutral elements, subtraction and division as inverse operations, representation of operations (function machine). (E) Roman, Egyptian, etc. number systems, other number bases, relations on the naturals.

3. Geometric foundations I

Sets of lines, points, ... Subsets and properties (open, convex, ...), basic shapes and solids (triangle, rectangle, circle, cube, sphere,...), perpendicular and parallel, representation of properties using arrow diagrams and tables, intersection and union of point sets, nets for simple solids. (E) linear graphs (transport nets, footpaths), surfaces (torus, Möbius band), construction of simple geometrical patterns.

4. Magnitude

Basic units and comparison of length, mass, monetary value, time, area and time (but expressed with much use of 'Mengen'!).

Class 6 (N–W)

1. Divisors

Sets of divisors and multiples, gcd and lcm, division rules for 2, 4, 8, 5 and 10, the set of primes, Eratosthenes, congruence classes (and operations), divisibility rules 3 and 9, (E) sets of prime factors, Hasse diagram for 'divides', Euclid's algorithm.

2. Fractions

Classes of number pairs, set of fractions, ordering, the four operations, mixed and decimal fractions, operations with decimal fractions. (E) frequencies, probability (relative frequency), the slide rule.

3. Geometric foundations II

Relations between pairs of points and lines, constructions of perpendicular and angle bisectors (ruler and compass), line reflections and translations. (E) vectors as equivalence classes of translations, addition of vectors.

(It should be pointed out at this stage that the N–W Realschule syllabus dates from 1978 and is currently being revised. The Gymnasium syllabus was revised in 1984 and, as we shall see below, is nothing like as abstract or ambitious. Enquiries suggest that the teaching in schools does not reflect the manner in which the syllabus is described.)

Classes 7–10 (12–16, Baden–Württemberg)

In this key stage the syllabuses for the Hauptschule and the Realschule begin to differ significantly. In particular, the lower (Hauptschule) pupils devote a greater proportion of their time to utilitarian arithmetic. For example, in Class 7 the number of hours allotted is: Hauptschule 48, Realschule 24. In general, the Realschule students are exposed to some deeper mathematical ideas and we **briefly** summarise these below.

Class 7 Thales theorem, tangents to circles, (E) angle properties of n–gons and circles; multiplication of sums (preparatory to binomial formula in Class 8), (E) inequalities; graphical representation of variables directly and inversely proportional.

Class 8 Congruence theorems, prisms (but note that π is held back until Class 9 and not, as in the Hauptschule, introduced in Class 8); linear equations in two variables, (E) graphical solutions; (E) reading of tables, statistics, graphs, etc.

Class 9 Use of calculators, standard (scientific) notation, real numbers, square and cube roots, graph of quadratic functions, (E) powers with rational exponents, other roots (using calculator), using a calculator program to obtain an approximate root; enlargements, π as an irrational (also area, arc, sector), volumes.

Class 10 (Note this class has no counterpart in the B–W Hauptschule)

1. Trigonometry (36 hours)

Sine and cosine to 360°, tangent to 90°, simple relations, graphical representation, right–angled triangles, sine and cosine theorems.

2. Advanced mensuration (32 hours)

Pyramids, circular cones (surface area, volume), sphere, compound solids, solids of rotation.

3. Practical calculations (20 hours)

Percentage and interest, linear and exponential growth (including biological examples).

12 hours are devoted to assessment.

Classes 7–10 North Rhine–Westphalia

Again the syllabus is presented in a '1960's modern' style. The underlying mathematics is not dissimilar to that in the B–W syllabus. However, functions and relations are given very much more stress in Grade 9. Exponents (and scientific notation) are not introduced until Grade 10 and their use in logarithms is given considerable emphasis. Trigonometry is restricted to acute angles for students following the 'basic' course (including the appropriate sine and cosine theorems).

In general, therefore, the N–W Realschule syllabus places more emphasis on mathematical ideas than on the acquisition of competence in more limited areas. However, this syllabus can give no indication of what curriculum is implemented in schools.

The N–W Realschule offers an 11th grade course for mathematics/science specialists. This comprises: sets and Boolean algebra (including some logic, De Morgan's Laws, modus ponens, etc. and applications to networks); linear optimisation; probability and statistics (mean, variance, s.d., combinations, binomial distribution, hypothesis testing, Monte Carlo methods); algebraic structure (groups (permutations, geometric transformations, symmetries, number sets, residue classes,...), generators, cyclic groups, isomorphism, factor groups, subgroups, Lagrange's theorem,...).

Gymnasium

The Baden–Württemberg Gymnasium course consists of four years during which the same mathematics is taken by all (120 hours in Class 5, 150 in Class 6, 120 in Class 7 and 150 in Class 8), followed by three years in which the science and language streams study the topic to different depths, and two years (Classes 12 and 13) in which both basic, advanced and extended, specialist courses are offered.

The syllabus is presented by year, and the number of hours to be spent on particular areas of the syllabus and on assessment are recommended.

An interesting feature of the syllabus is the way in which occasional historical references are built in, for example, to Adam Ries, the first popular author in the vernacular (a contemporary of Robert Recorde).

Class 5 (10–11)

This does not differ in any significant way from the syllabus for the Realschule. There is the occasional addition, eg sequences are optional extras, and somewhat more bizarrely, Gymnasium pupils are expected to know the value of 25^2. However, in essence, transfer between schools should cause no problem at the end of this stage.

Class 6 (11–12)

Now emphases begin to change between the Gymnasium and the Realschule. Thus in the former more time is devoted to vulgar fractions (44 against 36 hours), less to decimals (20 against 26), more to geometry and less to calculations concerning quantities. In general, syllabus differences concern depth rather than new topics, although π is introduced and point–symmetry. Optional topics include Euclid's algorithm, residue classes and symmetry in space.

Class 7 (12–13)

By this stage the emphasis on commercial, everyday arithmetic has gone from the Gymnasium course. It is evident that different assumptions are being made concerning the way in which Gymnasium and Realschule students are expected to use mathematics in later years.

Proportionality (30 hours): direct and inverse, rule of three, percentage, (optional: interest)

Basic constructions in geometry (28 hours): symmetry in a line, bisectors and medians, isosceles triangles, orthogonality, point symmetry, parallels (angle properties), angle sum of triangle and quadrilateral, Thales theorem, various ruler and compass constructions, circles and tangents.

Rational numbers (30 hours): ordering, operations (optional: comparison of structures of **N** , **Z** and **Q**).

Algebraic expressions and equations (16 hours): variables, constructing formulae, linear equations and inequalities in one unknown.

Class 8 (13–14)

(The Gymnasium and Realschule syllabuses have now diverged substantially.)

Expressions, equations and inequalities (45 hours): brackets, quadratics, simple rational functions, equivalence of formulae (examples from Physics), linear equations and inequalities (optional: binomial formula for $n > 2$, Pascal's triangle).

Congruence and figures (45 hours): isometries and their properties, congruent figures, congruence theorems for triangles, in– and circumcircles, centroid and circumcentre, constructing triangles, quadrilaterals and their classification (optional: group properties of isometries, representation of isometries in terms of line reflections).

Linear functions and systems of equations (30 hours): cartesian coordinates, $y = mx+c$, solution of linear equations, graphs of linear inequalities in two variables, systems of two equations in two unknowns, applications, simple linear systems with more than two variables (optional: linear programming relations).

Probability (14 hours): experiments with random outcomes, events, tree diagrams, probabilities, relative frequencies.

Class 9 (14–15)

At this stage two mathematics courses are offered: for science and for arts students.

Science option

Real numbers (25 hours): need for reals, representation, number line, operations, comparison of **R**, **Z**, **Q**, **R**, square roots (approximations and operations with square roots), variance and standard deviation.

Quadratic and square root functions (15 hours): $ax^2 + bx + c$ and its graph, $\sqrt{x}$ and its graph, simple maxima and minima.

Quadratic and square root equations (27 hours): solution of quadratics, factorisation, discriminant, equations involving square roots, applications (eg intersection of line and parabola) (optional: quadratic inequalities).

Area and Pythagoras (27 hours): rectangle, parallelogram, triangle and trapezium, Pythagoras and converse, construction of square roots (optional: Pythagorean triplets, investigations on micro).

Similarities (25 hours): enlargements and their properties, ratio theorems, similarity transformations and their properties, similarity of figures (in particular, triangles), applications.

Either intuitive vectors (15 hours): addition, scalar multiplication, linear combination, components

Or elements of informatics: analysis of problems, algorithms, programs.

Languages stream

This offers an abbreviated version of the science syllabus eg variance and s.d., factorisation of quadratics, similar triangles are now options. However, the elements of informatics unit is now compulsory and vectors are omitted.

Class 10 (15–16)

Science stream

'Power' functions (34 hours): rational exponents, n^{th} roots, calculations with powers, simple equations, real exponents, standard (scientific) notation, polynomial division (all using 'plausible' explanations).

The exponential and logarithmic functions (20 hours): simple equations, applications (growth, pH values, etc.)

Circle calculations (10 hours): π , perimeter, area, arcs, applications (eg nautical mile).

Representation and mensuration of bodies (30 hours): parallel projection and properties, volume and surface area of prisms, circular cylinders, pyramids, sphere, etc., applications.

Trigonometric functions (40 hours)
Sine, cosine, tangent; properties and representation, sine, cosine and addition theorems, trigonometric equations, applications, eg harmonic motion, surveying.

Language stream The same five sections are covered in less depth (in particular, geometric drawing is omitted): the hours allotted are 25, 12, 7, 9 and 25 respectively.

Class 11 (16–17)

Science stream

Lines, segments and angles in cartesian coordinates (10 hours): distance of two points, midpoint, line through two points, general form of line, angle between two lines, orthogonality.

Functions (12 hours): domain and range, intervals, representation of functions (graphs, tables, ordered pairs), revision of linear, power, trigonometric and modulus functions, operations on functions, rational functions.

Limits, continuity, differentiability (30 hours): series, limits of a function for $x \to \infty$, $x \to -\infty$ and $x \to x_0$, theorems on limits, continuity, differentiation (geometrically), derived functions of x^n ($n \in N$, $n = 1, ½$), sums and products, difference between differentiability and continuity, higher derivatives, $\sin kx$, $\cos kx$, (optional: APs and GPs, Principle of Induction).

Polynomials (28 hours); odd and even functions, graphical symmetries, zeros, factorisation of polynomials with help of known zeros, monotonicity, extreme values, max and min, geometric interpretation of second derivative, points of inflection, limits as $x \to \pm \infty$, graphs, applications, (optional: Horner's method).

Option (28 hours)

Either Boolean algebra: truth tables, set algebra, Boolean algebra, duality principle, switching circuits,
Or Complex numbers: polar form, operations, algebraic structure of **C** , embedding of **R** in **C** , n^{th} roots

Or Conic sections: ellipse, hyperbola, parabola as plane sections, focus directrix properties of parabola, sum and difference properties of ellipse and hyperbola (Dandelin's sphere), tangents.

Language stream

The first four sections are studied in a less deep manner (10, 12, 30 and 28 hours); the optional unit is replaced by a review and revision of the work done in Classes 9 and 10 (28 hours). Note that both language and science streams have 120 hours allotted to mathematics in Class 11. (12 hours are assigned to assessment.)

Classes 12 and 13 (17–19)

In these two classes students may take a basic or an enriched course. The basic course comprises: integration (primitives), fundamental theorem of calculus, applications, further differentiation (product and quotient rules, exponential function, natural logarithms), applications (optional: integration by parts, volumes) and **either** coordinate geometry: vectors, lines and planes in parametric form, circle and sphere, ellipse as image of circle under an affine transformation **or** statistics (probability (conditional probability is an option), binomial distribution, significance tests).

The extended course delves more deeply into the differential and integral calculus (integration by substitution, area and volume, inverse functions, trigonometric functions (differential equation for harmonic motion and series for sine and cosine are options), exp and ln as inverse functions, limits of $x^r e^x$ etc., applications to growth and decay (L'Hospital and series for e^x are options)), iteration (Newton–Raphson) (computer applications optional).

It then offers analytic geometry and geometry in two alternative courses, one stressing the former, one the latter. (Essentially, this means one takes the 'other' option of the basic course and deepens understanding of the previously selected option.) New work involves systems of linear equations, vector spaces, affine and metric geometry in Euclidean space, affine transformations in the plane; and the foundations of probability (Kolmogorov, v. Mises), conditional probability, multiplication theorem, independent probabilities (Bayes theorem is optional), random variables, expectation, variance and s.d., Chebyshev's inequality, expectation and variance of $aX + b$ and $X + Y$, independence of random variables, binomial distribution (expectation and variance), Normal distribution, Φ, central limit theorem (Poisson optional), estimation of population parameters, hypothesis testing, (options: confidence intervals, goodness of fit).

Gymnasium: North Rhine–Westphalia

We shall present only a translation of the 'overview' of the mathematics syllabus for classes 5–10. The material is presented, as indicated, in two-year blocks.

Years	Algebra	Geometry	Statistics and Probability
5–6	Calculations with whole numbers, divisors and their properties, calculations with fractions, decimals	Fundamentals: basic shapes and solids, propaedeutical work on the isometries	Experiments with random outcomes, calculation of simple probabilities (tree and Venn diagrams)
7–8	Rational numbers, linear functions, linear equations and inequalities, systems of equations, equations involving quotients	Angle theorems in polygons, congruent figures, circle theorems, areas of basic shapes, volumes of prisms (0), motions in the plane (0)	Descriptive statistics, randomness and expectation (0)
9–10	Real numbers, quadratic functions, powers and exponential functions, inverse function, trigonometric functions, quadratic equations and inequalities	Pythagoras and related theorems, similarity, circle mensuration, volumes and surface area of basic solids (0)	Combinatorics with applications to probability

((0) denotes optional topic)

It will be seen then that, again, there are important differences between the syllabuses in B–W and N–W. Moreover the N–W Gymnasium programme (1984) is less abstract and set–oriented than is that Land's Realschule syllabus.

In classes 9–10 there are opportunities for pupils in N–W to take additional two-hour courses. One concentrates on revision and reinforcement of the basic course, the other on laying down foundations for further study. In the latter the teacher selects appropriate themes from mathematical modelling, computer–oriented problem–solving, optimisation, descriptive statistics and line of best fit (no calculus), Boolean algebra, complex numbers and conformal transformations, nomograms, descriptive geometry, coordinate geometry (linear and quadratic forms).

GREECE

Age (yr)	Grade			
5-6	K	Pre-school		
6-7	1	Primary School		
7-8	2			
8-9	3			
9-10	4			
10-11	5			
11-12	6			
12-13	7	Secondary I (Gymnasium)		
13-14	8			
14-15	9			
15-16	10	Secondary II (Lyceum)		
16-17	11	General	Technical Vocational	Integrated
17-18	12			

Notes

1. The "integrated" type of lyceum offers a wide variety of subjects, more practical than the "general" (the type usually attended by the university-bound), and more advanced than the "technical-vocational". About 1 in 4 of post-15 students still in school are in the "technical-vocational" institutions.

2. The national curriculum is common to state and private schools.

GREECE

The Greek national curriculum is presented in considerable detail at the primary school level with guidance on ordering and methodology. As yet the secondary school curricula are given in a sparer, more formal manner. Moreover, the syllabuses for the six years of primary education are prescriptive in setting out the time to be devoted to teaching particular areas of content. In some cases guidance can be very specific, for example, for 11–12 year–olds, one hour should be devoted to 'prime and composite numbers' and one to representing a composite number as a product of primes. In the Gymnasium the specification is by content to be covered in each year, although in the Lyceum (Lykeion) this is broken down into two areas, algebra and geometry, each with its own allocation of hours.

There are no specific suggestions for dealing with differences of ability and attainment between students in a particular age group. The same textbooks are used in all schools and are issued free of charge.

The impression is given of a rather ambitious, formally–taught syllabus in which many topics are repeated (rather than merely revised) at different stages. A marginal reference to the calculator is made in the syllabus for Grade 8 (13–14) of the Gymnasium and its use is now recommended in Grade 10 (15–16). The use of micros varies widely: their use is more common in the Integrated and Technical–Vocational Lyceums and in private schools. The syllabuses are still much influenced by the innovations of the 1960s; the language of sets occurs in the primary school curriculum whilst algebraic structures such as groups, rings and fields are taught in the Lyceum. In some ways there would seem to be an epistemological gap between the principles and the goals of the curricula for the primary school and for the gymnasium.

Assessment in primary schools is internal (and was, until recently, informal – now grades will be awarded in the last two years) and, in general, there is automatic promotion from class to class. Assessment in the secondary schools is internal (apart from the examination for entrance to higher education), but now promotion is no longer automatic, there is grading, and in some cases students must resit examinations in September. Private tuition for secondary–school students is very common.

Primary school

Ist year (6–7)

Here certain pre–mathematical concepts (order, size and language (eg right, left, more than, less than)) are introduced before more specifically mathematically concepts are taught (1–1 correspondence, sets, number). The ideas of measurement (length, time, area, money, capacity) are introduced, but the time devoted to this (6 teaching hours) would not seem to be sufficient to encourage much in the way of practical activities. Considerably more time (25 hours) is devoted to the numbers 1–5 and the notions of addition and subtraction as applied to these. Twenty eight hours are devoted to numbers 1–10 (now with the additional operation of multiplication introduced via the union of a number of disjoint sets of equal cardinality). Finally, 30 hours are spent on the numbers 1–20 (with the new concept of a 'half'). Six hours are also spent considering such geometric notions as straight line and curve, and that of dimension (eg cube v. square).

2nd Year (7–8)

First year work is now extended in a consistent manner: 24 hours are devoted to the ordinal and cardinal numbers up to 100, the concept of place value, and to the common fractions $^1/_4$, $^1/_2(=^2/_4)$ and $^3/_4$. Fifty eight hours are then spent on the four arithmetical operations applied to these numbers (division being introduced through the partitioning of a set) and to their use in the solution of problems. The commutative and associative properties of addition are introduced. Again, time (26 hours in all) is devoted to gaining further geometrical notions and language (circle, square, rectangle, triangle, measurement of length, width, area – using first non–standard and then standard units) and to extending the child's range of 'pre–mathematical' and 'basic–mathematical' concepts (eg the partitioning of sets). Four hours are set aside for a propaedeutical introduction to some ideas of probability, ie, the playing of games and the tabulation of results.

3rd Year (8–9)

Set vocabulary is developed (subsets, plus some revision and extension on the partitioning of sets), standard units of measurement introduced, and the numbers up to 1000 added to the child's 'school–reckoning' set. Again, little time (6 hours) is spent on measurement as against 51 hours on operations on numbers up to 1000, including multiplication by two digit numbers, and division by single digit numbers. Part of this time is also spent on solutions of problems and the development of mental arithmetic. In this year, ten hours are spent on fractions (thirds, eighths and sixths), on comparisons between them, on equivalent fractions and on problems concerning fractions. Five hours are given over to further ground work on probability and the construction of simple statistical tables. Six hours are spent (mainly revision) on plane geometrical shapes.

4th Year (9–10)

The numbers considered become larger (up to 10^6) but are still bounded. Addition and subtraction are now seen as inverse operations, as are multiplication and division. Multiplication and division by multiples of ten are given special consideration as are different algorithms for addition and subtraction. Fractions are considered in some detail and generality. The addition and subtraction of fractions with the same denominator is introduced and there is some work on fractions with different denominators. A link is made between fractions and probabilities and the conversion of mixed numbers to fractions is considered.

Measurement is now accorded more importance; weight, length, time, money, area and volume are all introduced (metric units) together with temperature.

Set language is developed (leading towards intersection), decimals are introduced by using fractions with denominators which are powers of 10 and the addition and subtraction of such decimals explored.

Geometrical concepts are revised in greater depth and much new vocabulary introduced (names of common 3–dimensional objects, further 2–dimensional shapes (eg rhombus)), triangles are classified (equilateral,...) and notions such as perimeter and angle (right–angled, acute) are developed.

5th Year (10–11)

Numbers over 10^6, representation in bases other than 10, and the classical representations of numbers in Greece and Rome are considered together with divisors and multiples of integers.

Mixed 'measures'(eg 1 hour 12 mins 4 secs) and the conversion to fractions; addition and subtraction.

Positive rational numbers are now considered in depth, including ordering, conversion from, say, decimal to fractional representation, and the four operations on rationals in their fractional form.

Many geometrical notions are developed including: the measurement and construction of angles, various polygons (including consideration of their perimeters), parallel and intersecting lines in the plane, the areas of parallelograms and triangles, drawing simple objects to scale, and terms relating to the circle (centre, radius, diameter, arc, chord, inscribed regular polygons).

Graphical representation and the idea of mean (average) are taught in statistics.

6th Year 11–12

Algebra is introduced: for example, one hour is assigned to 'numbers expressed by letters' and two to equations of the type $ax + b = c$ and $ax - b = c$. Similar, brief acquaintances are provided with primes and factorization into primes. Powers are introduced, including powers of 10, and standard notation with positive exponents. One hour is spent on the meaning of 'if... then'.

Eighteen hours are devoted to linking measurement and decimal representation of numbers. Work on geometrical construction is included.

Other geometrical work is mainly 3–dimensional and includes work on the construction of standard shapes, their surface area and volume.

Four hours are given over to the presentation of statistical data through diagrams and tables.

A major component (33 hours) on ratio serves to introduce such basic arithmetical notions as proportion and percentage, and problems relating to these.

Secondary Education I (Gymnasium)

The primary school curriculum is, therefore, ambitious and perhaps not surprisingly, since there is no attempt to cater for children of different ability and attainment, much content has to be repeated, often more formally in the early Gymnasium years.

Year 1 (12–13) (4 hrs per week)

The syllabus is divided into seven sections:

1. Natural and decimal numbers: variables and equations, four arithmetical operations, distributive law, conventions on the priority of operations, gcd's and lcm's, powers of numbers, estimation.

2. Measurement: number line; lengths, area and volumes (rectangle, square, cuboid, cube), measures of money, time and weight.

3. Fractions: concept of fractions, equivalence, order, translation from decimal to fractional form and vice-versa, operations with fractions, problems involving percentages, relative frequency and relevant graphs.

4. Basic geometric concepts: point, line, plane, segments, distance, parallel and perpendicular (including construction), distance of a point from a line; circle (radius, chord, arc, diameter); construction of perpendicular bisector of a segment.

5. Angles: concept, different types, measurement; angles formed by intersecting lines; line cutting parallel lines; ruler and compass constructions of an angle equal to a given one and of angle-bisector.

6. Shapes in the plane: triangles and the different types, angle sum, construction (SSS, ASA, SAS); parallelograms and the different types, properties of parallelogram; area of parallelogram, triangle and trapezium.

7. Rational numbers: positive and negative numbers, integers, rationals, absolute value, number line, addition and subtraction.

Year 2 (13–14) (4 hrs per week)

1. Rational numbers: concept, absolute value, ordering, four operations, powers with natural or integer exponent, scientific notation, decimal representation.

2. Equations and inequalities: solution of linear equations, transposition of formulae, problems; inequalities, solutions of algebraic inequalities, applications.

3. Real numbers: Pythagoras, square roots, irrationals, reals, number line, operations, coordinates of a point in the plane.

4. Trigonometric functions of an acute angle: ratios in straight-line segments, ratios in a right-angled triangle; sine, cosine, tangent; trigonometric tables;

applications.

5. Functions: concept, graphical representation, direct and inverse proportionality, $y = ax + b$, $y = a/x$, applications.

6. Statistics: main types of diagrams; some basic notions – sample, population, frequency; histograms; mean, median.

7. Symmetrical shapes: point and line symmetry and properties of figures having these.

8. The circle: angle properties; regular inscribed polygons leading to area and circumference of circle.

9. 3–D shapes: relationship of lines and planes in 3–D; prism, cylinder, pyramids, cone, sphere and their surface areas and volumes.

3rd Year (14–15) (4 hours per week in the first term, then 3 hours per week)

1. Real numbers: operations, powers, roots, order.

2. Algebraic expressions: monomials, similar terms, multiplication of polynomials, identities, factorisation of quadratics, rational algebraic expressions, applications.

3. Equations: linear and quadratic equations, solutions, equations with fractions.

4. Functions: concept, $y = ax$, $y = ax+b$, $y = ax^2$, $y = ax^2+bx+c$, $y = a/x$.

5. Statistics: revision, frequency (cumulative), variance, concept of probability.

6. Congruence and similarity: revision of triangles, congruent triangles, segments between parallel lines, Thales' Theorem, similar polygons and triangles, areas and volumes of similar shapes.

7. Trigonometry: acute angle, general angle, supplementary angle, relationship of trigonometric functions, sine and cosine rules.

8. Systems of equations and inequalities: systems of linear equations, algebraic solutions, linear inequalities.

9. Vectors: concept, coordinates, addition, subtraction and scalar multiplication of vectors.

10. Sphere: revision, relative positions of sphere and plane, the earth as a sphere.

Secondary Education II (Lyceum)

The route to university mathematics is usually through the General Lyceum although there are routes through the two other types of Lyceum. Again, there is a considerable amount of revision of material from the previous stage of education, but it is now treated in a more deductive way. Following changes to the lower secondary school curriculum, that for the Lyceum is now being revised. Below we give the new syllabus for the 1st year and the unrevised syllabuses for the two later years. The major change in the 1st year syllabus is the reduction in formalism, eg omission of truth tables and the axioms for an ordered field.

1st Year (15–16) (5 hrs per week changing to 4 hrs in the second semester)

The reals: operations, powers with integer and rational exponents, roots, order, identities, absolute value, intervals
Elementary set theory (set, subset, union, intersection, difference, complement)
Real functions, graphs, polynomials, operations, composition, monotonicity
Linear equations, solutions, inequalities, systems of equations and inequalities, use of determinants, graphical solutions, applications to linear programming
Quadratics, equations that can be transformed into linear or quadratic equations, systems of equations and inequalities, graphical solutions
Bound and free vectors, coordinates, operations, projection, scalar (inner) product, geometrical applications
Probabilistic experiments, definitions of probability (frequency, symmetry), additive rule, mutually exclusive events, multiplicative rule, combinations and applications to probability theory
Trigonometric circle; sine, cosine and tangent functions, equations and inequalities
Basic concepts of geometry – point, line, plane, segment, comparison of straight line segments; circle, arc, angle, operations, comparison of angles and arcs; triangles, congruence, inequalities in a triangle and between two triangles; perpendicularity; parallelism, parallelograms, midpoints of sides of triangle, trapeziums; angles in circles, chord and tangent properties, cyclic and circumscribed quadrilaterals; Thales' theorem, similarity, properties of bisectors and medians, Pythagoras' theorem, metric relations in a triangle; area, regular polygons, mensuration of circle

2nd Year (16–17) (5 hours per week: 3 algebra, 2 geometry)

Polynomial equations (factorization, Horner's method etc.)
Real functions (graphical representation, transformation of axis system, gradients of lines and properties; max and min; odd, even, periodic, monotonic, graphical solutions)
Trigonometry (A + B and 2A formulae, sinA + sinB etc, trig. equations; sine and cosine rules, applications)
Sequences and series (graphical representation, definition by recurrence relation, APs, partial sums, GPs, limits)
Exponential and logarithmic functions
Statistics (sampling, cumulative frequency, pie charts, standard deviation)
Elementary analysis (limits of sequences, derivatives, basic differentiation, maxima and minima)
Basic theorems on ratios of lengths and similarity (Thales, Pythagoras), areas, regular polygons, angles, (including dihedral angles) and further revision of geometrical notions including 3–D geometry and shapes.

3rd Year (17–18)

Mathematics can be dropped at this level or taken as a non–examinable subject by those wishing to study, say, medicine at university. Not all topics (eg, combinatorics) are in the final examination syllabus.

For those specialising in mathematics (would–be scientists, engineers, etc) the syllabus is:
Matrices and simultaneous equations (Gauss, determinants, inverse matrices, solution via inverse matrices, Cramer's rule)
Groups and rings (concepts and examples, subgroups)
Vector spaces (concepts, subspace, bases, dimension, application to solution of simultaneous linear equations)
Complex numbers (graphical and trigonometrical expression, modulus and argument, conjugates, De Moivre, n^{th} roots of unity)
Statistics (mainly revision with some deepening)
Combinatorics (cartesian product, cardinality, combinations and permutations, Binomial theorem)
Probability (including conditional probability, independent events)
Calculus (revision of work on functions, sequences, limits; limit of a function, continuity; limits of sums and products; exp and log functions; derivative (including composite functions); max and min; Rolle and L'Hospital; integration, applications to area and volume).

Those specializing in technical and business subjects follow a similar syllabus treated at a lower level. Topics such as groups, rings, vector spaces and complex numbers are omitted. Certain university courses (eg those for would–be primary school teachers) are open to those following either of the two mathematics courses and also to those who have not taken mathematics as an examinable subject.

HUNGARY

Age (yr)	Grade			
5-6	K	Kindergarten		
6-7	1	Primary / Elementary School		
7-8	2			
8-9	3			
9-10	4			
10-11	5			
11-12	6			
12-13	7			
13-14	8			
14-15	9	Gymnasium	Vocational secondary	Vocational 2-3 years
15-16	10			
16-17	11			
17-18	12			

Notes

1. Child care starts as early as 6 months (offered on a limited scale) and Kindergarten covers the 3–6 age range. In principle, the last year of Kindergarten is compulsory, and Kindergartens are, in fact, attended by practically all children in urban areas and the majority from rural environments.

2. Over 90% of children who complete elementary school continue their studies in 14+ schools; the distribution being (roughly) in the ratios, Gymnasium 1, Vocational Secondary 1, Restricted Vocational 2. Possibly in the region of 10% of the age cohort fail to complete elementary school.

3. Twelve or more gymnasiums offer specialized mathematics courses. Teachers in these have considerable freedom concerning content.

4. The vocational secondary schools offer a variety of specializations and also provide a gateway to tertiary education.

HUNGARY

Hungary has a rich mathematical and pedagogical tradition. Although a small country, its national curriculum is, therefore, of special interest.

One striking feature to note is the way in which the Hungarian syllabus had to be reduced in the late '70s and early '80s, largely in response to the cuts made in the time devoted to mathematics, following the reduction of the school week to five days.

Other features of the Hungarian system worthy of mention include the recent emergence of independent schools (elementary, gymnasiums, and vocational secondary schools run by religious groups or as private concerns) which may diverge from the national curriculum. Schooling in state schools is free but text and exercise books are not always supplied free of charge, although this has recently become an aim.

Teachers of grades 1–4 are 'class' teachers and not mathematics specialists. However, teachers in later grades are specialists. As in, for example, Italy, it is an aim that a specialist teacher should be responsible for the same pupils throughout a 'key stage' i.e. grades 5–8 and grades 9–12. (As in Italy, the mathematics teacher will very often teach physics too.)

Assessment of pupils is continuous and internal with the exception of the school–leaving 'matura' examination.

In theory the school curriculum is very rigidly predicated. Until recently it was only in mathematics that teachers had a choice of textbook. The result is that the curriculum is effectively defined by means of tasks set out in reference and textbooks and worksheets, rather than by the list of contents given below, or, indeed, the guidelines which accompany them. The alternative series of secondary school mathematics texts is written to the same syllabus, but offers different teaching approaches. A third series of texts, which assumes the provision and use of micros, has recently begun to appear.

Very recently, schools have been given the opportunity to make local changes to the basic national curriculum.

As in most European countries, nursery education, although not compulsory, is almost universal. Indeed, in Hungary specific guidelines and objectives are provided for mathematics teaching within the kindergarten. It aims:

to develop an ability to count (including addition and subtraction if possible);
to observe geometrical objects (both planar and 3–D);
to draw simple logical conclusions (eg, to group by attributes).

It is expected that these objectives will be attained through activity methods making use of simple apparatus.

The eight–year elementary school curriculum is still based upon one developed in the 1960s by the late Tamás Varga, although it is currently again under review. A significant feature is its attempt to present a unified view of mathematics from even the earliest years through the provision of experiences in many areas of mathematics, such as geometry, algebra, logic, and probability. Such propaedeutical experiences are not necessarily linked with explicit attainment targets for learning. The treatment is of a 'spiral' nature; in general, with clear goals for each encounter with a subject (eg, fractions with a unit numerator in grade 2, multiples of these (two thirds, four thirds,...) in grade 3, and so on). This sought–for unity cannot be represented by a published syllabus. It must be borne in mind in what follows.

The co–ordinated subject matter is divided for syllabus purposes into five main themes:

sets and logic,
arithmetic and algebra,
relations, functions and series,
geometry and measurement,
combinatorics, probability and statistics.

Below we give an indication of how each theme is treated in each grade (the figures in parentheses indicate grade levels). Five hours a week are devoted to mathematics in Grades 1–3, four hours thereafter.

A. Sets and logic

This section begins with work on classification and organisation (eg classification of planar shapes by number of sides, holes, etc. (2)), with making statements (and their negation) about objects, and by seeing how simple open sentences can become true or false depending on the object, personal name, etc, chosen to replace the variable (1, 2). This last work is developed in Grades 3 and 4 through the use of statements containing numbers. At this stage the notion of intersection (properties in common) is introduced together with preliminary work on 'and', 'or', 'all the ...' and 'there are some ...' Some simple equations and inequalities are solved by trial and improvement methods. Classification according to one or more criteria (eg symmetry) is covered in Grades 5 and 6 and abstract statements written in words (no mathematical symbols at that stage). A first introduction is made to 'if ... then' constructions and to the concept of equivalent statements. Open sentences containing two or more variables are considered. In the final two grades (7, 8), statements are grouped according to common meaning and algebraic expressions classified according to their solution set (ie a distinction is drawn between equations and identities). Notions of proof ('it follows from ... that ...') are developed with examples from number theory, geometry and algebra.

The aim is that at all stages (here and elsewhere in the elementary school curriculum), topics introduced earlier are revised and seen in greater depth.

B. Arithmetic and algebra

The ideas of counting and measuring are built up gradually, first using small numbers, then numbers up to a hundred (2), thousands (3) and millions (4). Addition and subtraction are introduced in Grade 1 and multiplication (repeated addition) and division (dividing into equal parts) in Grade 2. The four operations are re-considered (together with groupings such as 630 = (120 x 5) + (6 x 5)) in Grade 3, whilst in later grades (with 'above- average' classes) multiplication is seen as a binary-operation (rather than as repeated addition). Early (2) emphasis is laid on counting in twos, threes and tens thus strengthening the concept of place value. Simple fractions (half, one third, one quarter) are introduced in Grade 2 as are negative numbers (temperatures). Fractions with non-unit numerators are considered in Grade 3 and multiplication with fractions in Grade 6. Decimal fractions are introduced in Grade 5. The work on negative numbers is developed through debts and assets (3), to work on the number line and operations in later grades (5-8). The question of exact and approximate values is raised in Grade 3 in connection with measurements and 'rounding off' is considered in Grade 4. Ratios are first introduced in Grade 4 and percentages in Grade 6. Powers are studied in Grade 5. In the higher grades (6-8), topics considered include terminating and recurring decimals, rational numbers, divisibility rules (by 2, 4, 5, 3 and 9), the solution of equations and inequalities, and factorisation ($a^2 - b^2 = (a-b)(a+b)$).

(Note: this brief outline of 'arithmetic' can give a misleading impression: entries correspond to the first introduction of a concept rather than when understanding of that notion is to be expected. An over-riding aim is to consider the general characteristics and inter–relationships of numbers, eg the properties of even numbers, ordering, primes, etc. These ideas are developed throughout the infant and junior grades, as are counting and estimating skills.)

C. Relations, functions and series

These are not viewed as themes to be learned, but as aids to perceiving and comprehending inter–relationships. Various ways of displaying relations and functions (arrow diagrams, tables, graphs) are explored (orally in Grades 1 and 2, more abstractly in later grades). Grade 6 includes direct proportionality; absolute value is introduced in Grade 5 and seen as a function in Grade 7. Work on graphs also includes drawing graphs from observed data; when it makes sense to connect plotted points by a line, etc.

D. Geometry and measurement

Grades 1–4 (6–10)

Much construction and drawing leading to familiarity with different geometrical features and shapes (identification and classification of types of triangles and quadrilaterals). Elementary transformations and symmetry (use of stencils), study of patterns (wallpaper, etc).

Grades 5–8 (11–14)

Two–dimensional shapes and their construction (Euclidean methods). Three–dimensional bodies. Transformations and symmetry (intuitively only). Cartesian coordinates (and simple examples of the use of bearings and distance).

Practical measurement is developed from Grade 1 onwards; first length then, eg mass, time, capacity. Later, methods for determining area, volume, angles leading to mensuration formulae and examples.

E. Combinatorics, Probability and Statistics

(Because of its special interest, we describe this area of the curriculum in somewhat greater detail.)

Grade 1 (6–7)

Arranging objects in different sequences and making selections by means of activities and drawings. Identification and distinction of presented alternatives. Differentiating the concepts "definite", "probable but not certain" and "impossible". Getting acquainted with data collection while becoming more familiar with the numbers.

Grade 2 (7–8)

Listing and counting all pairs of elements in a given set. Pairing the elements of two sets. Recording the outcomes of random experiments. Counting the occurrencies (frequencies). Distinguishing between varying degrees of "probable but not certain" events.

Grade 3 (8–9)

Solving simple tasks involving combinations by means of activities and drawing. Searching for possible cases when making observations and performing experiments, and classifying them according to their likelihood. Collecting and recording data and results of measurements and experiments. Representing such data in tables and graphs. Activities to prepare for the introduction of the arithmetic mean.

Grade 4 (9–10)

Finding all possible combinations by means of arrangements in tables or using tree-diagrams. Establishing the number of all possibilities either by actual calculation or by estimation. Representing frequencies by bar–diagrams. Guessing the frequencies in a given number of repetitions of a random experiment. Comparison of the guesses with actual results. Selecting the most frequent element of a dataset. Location parameters and their meaning. Calculating the average of two or more integers.

Grades 5–6 (10–11, 11–12)

Calculating the arithmetic mean of several numbers. Relative frequencies as fractions, tenths and percentages. Evaluating the results of statistical experiments. Calculating the probabilities in simpler cases. Comparing relative frequencies with assumed or calculated probabilities.

Grade 8 (13–14)

Solving combinatorial problems related to other areas of mathematics in this grade, eg number of diagonals in an n–gon, number of divisors of a positive integer.

Statistics: observing correlated data (eg height–weight), graphical representation. Simple exercises in probability.

[Remark: Because of various pressures, this area (ie probability and statistics) is often neglected at the upper primary level; indeed, what was previously stipulated for Grade 7 is now no longer in the texts.]

The elementary school curriculum has, then, many interesting features.

Unfortunately, the secondary school syllabuses would seem to demonstrate both the defects of this undifferentiated elementary school curriculum and also an inability to capitalise on its achievements.

Vocational schools

Many of the 50% of the age cohort who attend the two– or three–year vocational schools would not appear to have comprehended much of the elementary school curriculum. Reputedly, therefore, the greater part of the three–year programme comprises re–teaching, revision and elaboration of elementary school material. The vocational schools assume a variety of forms; in some, for example, two days a week are spent obtaining practical work experience.

Mathematics is allotted four hours in each two–week unit in the first year, five in the second and four in the somewhat shorter final year.

The following are the major themes to be revised or developed:

Number

Basic skills with rationals, powers with integer exponents, square roots; ratio, proportion, percentages; arithmetical mean; divisibility, primes, factorizing given numbers.

Algebra

Simple equations in one and two unknowns; algebraic multiplication (eg $(a + b)^2$, $(a + b)(a - b)$).

Functions

Linear functions. Examples of non–linear functions, eg quadratic, exponential, growth (graphical approach).

Geometry

Characteristics of 2–D shapes; circumference and area; congruence and similarity; Pythagoras; trigonometric functions in a right–angled triangle.
Three dimensional figures (prisms, cylinders, spheres,...), properties; formulae for surface area and volumes.

Worksheets are provided containing examples of how this material is applied in specific employment areas, eg there are different worksheets for students interested in, for instance, lathe–turning, plumbing and the clothing industries.

Vocational Secondary School

Whereas the three–year vocational school aims to train competent tradesmen, the four or five–year 'industrial vocational secondary school' has more ambitious aims. Its students can obtain the 'matura', the school–leaving certificate which can lead to tertiary education.

The weekly number of mathematics lessons varies according to the specialization of the student. However, the time devoted to mathematics teaching has dropped in the last decade (eg in one typical school, from an average (over the four years) of 4 periods per week to 3.5 periods per week).

The curriculum of this type of school will, again, depend upon specialization. In some, such as those specializing in economics and computer technology, more mathematics is covered than is included even in the basic gymnasium course.

Gymnasium (General Secondary School)

As in the vocational secondary school, changes in timetabling for the curriculum as a whole have had profound effects upon mathematics teaching. In 1965 a minimum of 4.75 periods per week (averaged over four years) were devoted to mathematics. By 1985 this had dropped to 3.25 periods per week. (For those students specializing in mathematics the maximum number of periods per week dropped from 6.5 in 1979 to 5.75 in 1985.) The results have been considerable. In particular, differential and integral calculus which was in the 1965 curriculum is now no longer a compulsory component of the Gymnasium course. (Here it should be emphasised that the matura and university entrance examinations only demand knowledge of the basic, compulsory curriculum. Although the optional subjects aim to develop the students' ability to undertake tertiary study, they are not tested in the matura.)

Now it is likely that further changes will be made very shortly: already a working group has been set up to prepare a new syllabus. This will be done taking into account other probable reforms, eg the extension of pre–university education by one year and the raising of the school leaving age to 16.

We give below the compulsory part of the Gymnasium mathematics course. Additional mathematics topics can be studied in the final two years of the course. An optional course (3 to 5 hours extra per week) can be offered if 7 students request it, and, effectively, must be offered if 16 students do so. The course may comprise mathematics alone or mathematics with another subject. Topics include sequences and functions, differentiation and integration, further trigonometry and coordinate geometry, the elements of linear algebra, an introduction to computer science, probability and statistics.

However, there is evidence to suggest that in only a minority of schools is the compulsory syllabus printed below followed in its entirety.

First Grade (14–15, 160 periods)

(The number in brackets is the recommended number of lessons to be spent on the topic.)

Point sets (18): 1–, 2– and 3–D examples, characterization of sets by numbers, number line, coordinates, second degree curves satisfying certain properties.
Numbers and arithmetic (15): **N** , divisors, multiples, g.c.d., l.c.m., primes, unique factorisation (no proof), powers with integer exponents, standard (scientific) form.
Functions (18): mappings, basic notions, one–one correspondences, definition and representation (tables, graphs, Venn diagrams), linear, quadratic, reciprocal functions.
Algebra (43): Equations and inequalities, graphical and trial–and–improvement solutions, factorisation; basic identities; algebraic solution of linear equations and inequalities; polynomials; rational functions, simultaneous equations in two unknowns; word problems.
Basic Geometry (10): recapitulation; congruence and symmetry.
Reflection (20): reflections in a line (2–D), in a plane (3–D), Thales' Theorem

(circle), constructing triangles, proofs in geometry; reflections in a point (2–D and 3–D), parallelograms, 'notable' points and lines of triangles.
Translations and vectors (10): basic properties, invariant sets; notion of vectors, addition.
Basic properties of planar figures (4): classification, number of diagonals, convexity, regular polygons.
22 lessons to be devoted to evaluation and recapitulation.

Second Grade (15–16, 128 periods)

Extension of number concept (18): rational, decimals, irrationals as aperiodic decimals; Pythagoras, square roots, simpler equations containing square roots.
Rotations (14): basic properties, invariant figures; circle, circumference, angles, angles at centre and circumference (with proof), cyclic quadrilaterals.
Congruence in the plane (3): summing–up.
Similarity with applications (23): theorem of parallelism and proportional division of lengths, central similarities (homotheties), similarity in general, similarity transformations, similarity of plane figures, area properties, multiplying vectors by scalars, projections of vectors, coordinates, operations with coordinates, lengths of vectors.
Trigonometry (18): right–angled triangle, use of tables, use of trig. functions in calculating area and circumference, applications in physics.
Transformations and functions, quadratic equations (23): summary of work on transformations; transformations and graphing functions; monotonic and periodic functions, extreme values, zeros; solving quadratic equations graphically; algebraic solution with discussion of roots; word problems.
20 lessons of evaluation and recapitulation.

Third Grade (16–17, 96 lessons)

Powers, roots, logarithms (20): rational exponents (and, intuitively, irrational), exponential functions; properties of logarithms, bases, graphs, relation with exponential; use of tables; applications to equations involving log and exponential functions.
Applications of trigonometry (14): inner product, sine and cosine theorem, additional theorems; trig equations; applications.
Informatics and computer science (9): conjunction, disjunction, negation; calculations with approximate values; approximate solution of equations, algorithms and flow charts.
Coordinate geometry (23): coordinates and vectors; centre of gravity; distances; equations of straight line, circle, parabola; intersection of a circle and straight line,

tangents to circle and parabola.
Combinatorics (12): rudiments of graph theory; binomial coefficients and Pascal's triangle.
18 lessons of evaluation and recapitulation.

Fourth Grade (17–18, 84 lessons)

Series and sequences (22): general notions; AP and finite GP, summation, sum of $1^2 + 2^2 + ... + n^2$; proof by induction.
Mensuration (20): recapitulation for plane figures; surface area and volume of prism, cylinder, pyramid, cone and the sphere.
Systematic recapitulation of Gymnasium mathematics (42): basic notions of set theory and mathematical logic; numbers, algebraic laws; functions; equations and inequalities; geometric transformations; connecting geometric and algebraic notions; measurement; methods of mathematics – conclusions and proof; computational aids; philosophical questions of mathematics.

IRELAND

Age (yr)	Grade			
4-5	K	Primary school		
5-6	1			
6-7	2			
7-8	3			
8-9	4			
9-10	5			
10-11	6			
11-12	7			
12-13	8	Secondary	Vocational	Community
13-14	9			
14-15	10			
15-16	11	Upper Cycle		
16-17	12			

Notes

1. At the present time changes are being made both to the structure of the Irish system and to the curriculum.

2. Although education is compulsory only from age 6, primary schools serve children from 4 upwards. About 60% of 4 year–olds and almost all 5 year–olds attend primary schools.

3. About three–quarters of the age cohort take the Leaving Certificate. Others take vocational courses. The retention rate has increased rapidly in recent years, possibly due to economic conditions.

4. The new "Junior Certificate", taken at the end of the first cycle of secondary education, will be taken for the first time in 1992. This will necessitate changes to the structure of the second cycle, but these have still to be determined. An important decision must be made as to whether or not there will be separate academic and vocational qualifications offered at the end of the second cycle.

IRELAND

The Republic of Ireland can claim one peculiar link with mathematics education, for one of its founding fathers, de Valera, who was both Premier and President, was a former mathematics teacher. This, however, would seem to have had little effect on the mathematics curriculum!

Eight years of primary schooling are provided for children between the ages of 4 and 12, although education is compulsory only from age 6. Since children entering school later than usual still normally go into Junior Infants this means that grades do not always translate readily into ages. For that reason we have adopted a revised grade–age comparison in this national report. The usual K–12 numbering is used but has been brought forward a year. That is, Grade 12 is completed by most students at 17+.

Until 1967 there was a Primary Certificate Examination taken about age 12 at the end of Grade 7. Its abolition has had a considerable influence on the curriculum and has reduced some of the subject–centredness. Considerable time is still devoted, both at primary and secondary stages, to the teaching of the Irish language and this reduces the time available for other subjects such as mathematics. The medium of instruction for these is usually English.

It will be noted that even in the syllabuses revised in the mid–80s (and introduced into the lower secondary schools in 1987), the use of mathematical tables receives special attention. Calculators are not allowed in the national examination at the end of the first cycle of secondary education and, as a result, their use at this stage remains very limited. By contrast, calculators may be used in the Leaving Certificate examinations and their use in the upper secondary school is now becoming more widespread. Currently, consideration is being given to the greater use of calculators at all levels. Mandatory use of micros is, however, still avoided.

The primary school syllabus is set out in an attractively presented book, illustrated in colour. Chapters on the "Aims and Function" of primary education are followed by general chapters on "structure" and "organisation", before individual subjects are considered. The syllabus was first published in 1971 and the approach (and illustrations) recall English practice and innovations of the 1960s (and should not be dismissed on that account!). References are made, inter alia, to **Curriculum Bulletin** No.1, the Nuffield **Guides**, ATM's **Notes on Mathematics in Primary Schools**, and Williams and Shuard. Two syllabuses are offered, the ordinary (omitting sets – and which is dominant) and the alternative (which includes them). "The general approach suggested – guided experimentation and discovery – applies equally to both". The syllabuses are intended as an "indication of what may be undertaken ... [they] should be adapted or extended to suit the needs of schools, classes and individuals".

The material is presented in two year blocks.

Grades K–1 (ages 4–6)

The infant years are largely concerned with preparatory work. The emphasis is on free (ie guided) play and experiment which will supply a foundation for later work on size, shape, quantity, weight, ..., development of the relevant vocabulary, acquiring a feel for small numbers (up to 10) and for numerals, learning to sort and classify, and recognising simple relations (eg. greater or less than, is the same colour as). The teacher is offered various ideas for appropriate activities.

Grades 2–3 (ages 6–8)

The formal syllabus for this stage is brief – a mere half page. This is then followed by the equivalent of 12 or so pages of suggested activities.

The topics suggested are:

Number: addition up to 9+9, memorisation of addition facts, applications in context, notation of 2 and 3 digit numbers, place value, number patterns, associativity of addition, subtraction, number sentences with frames, pupil–contrived problems, grouping and counting in 2's and 3's etc. to 10's.

Activities: practical work to develop notions of length, weight, time, capacity, need for standard units, estimating and measuring, addition and subtraction based on these, practical use of halves and quarters, experience with 3– and 2–D shapes, making patterns in the plane and exploring symmetry, extending notion of area (with use of geoboard), shopping activities using money.

Language and recording: discussion, recording in the form of mathematical stories, use of block graphs.

Grades 4–5 (ages 8–10)

Number: multiplication as repeated addition, discovery and memorisation of multiplication tables up to 9x9, use of 100 square to explore number patterns, commutativity of multiplication, applications in context; notation for whole numbers, distributivity, multiplication of 2 and 3 digit numbers by a single digit number, estimation of products, multiplication by 20, 30, 40, ... leading to multiplication by any 2 digit number; short and long division; translation of simple problems involving four operations into number sentences with frames and vice–versa, knowledge of meaning of 1/2, 1/3, to 1/10 and 1/100, simple equivalence of fractions, applications in context, simple cases with numerator greater than one, simple applications of unitary method confined to whole numbers, decimals to two places, addition and subtraction.

Activities: further work on quantities and four operations, measurement of perimeter, need for unit of area, area of irregular and rectangular shapes, further 3D work especially with cube, ideas of direction (horizontal, vertical, parallel) leading to right angle, development of patterns leading to ideas of angle, use of geoboard and further work in symmetry, practical shopping and cross–curricular projects.

Language and recording: further work, bar charts and bar line graphs, introduction to scale (and maps), pictograms (ideographs).

Grades 6–7 (ages 10–12):

Number: sequence of numbers, odd and even, square, prime, composite, factor–isation using exponents, HCF and LCM, fractions as numbers, position on number line, equivalence, ordering of fractions, four operations, fractions as ratios; revision of notation for whole numbers and decimals, decimals as fractions and vice–versa, multiplication and division of decimals, percentages, elementary knowledge of directed numbers, further study of metric units, averages, speed; social arithmetic, calendar, timetables, simple interest, easy hire–purchase, discounts, profit and loss, practical applications (both pupil and teacher–contrived).

Algebra: number sequences, frame as a place–holder leading to use of letters, easy problems leading to simple equations.

Geometry: further work on topics introduced earlier, perpendicular and parallel lines (leading to parallelogram, square, rectangle, rhombus, etc), angles as a measure of rotation, set square, idea of degree, protractor, cardinal points of compass; cylinder, cone, pyramid, etc.; relationships between sides, angles and diagonals of geometric shapes, simple constructions, further work on symmetry, use of compass, area of rectangles, parallelograms, triangles and polygons using squared paper and geoboard, formula for rectangle, standard units of area.

Language and recording: further exercises on previous work, pie charts, trend graphs, linear graphs, cross–curricular projects, scale and maps in geography leading to coordinates (also latitude and longitude in geography).

The Alternative Syllabus, recommended only to those "au fait" with the subject content involved, includes work on sets and also some preliminary work on structure. Briefly, the additions are:

Infants: idea of cardinal number of a set.

Grades 2–3: naming elements, definition by attributes, complement, empty set and zero, union and intersection, addition based on union, arrow diagrams, zero as identity element under addition, closure, subtraction as inverse of addition, naturals not closed under subtraction.

Grades 4–5: cartesian product, multiplication and cartesian product, 1 as identity element, closure, different number bases, Venn diagrams, exercises on union and intersection.

Grades 6–7: union, intersection, difference, symmetric difference, use of symbols, relations, arrow diagrams, reflexivity, symmetry, transitivity, use of language in algebra (solution sets) and geometry (Venn diagrams to illustrate relationships between quadrilaterals).

Secondary education

Whereas the primary syllabuses reflect English practice, the 1970s and 1980s secondary school curriculum was influenced much more by innovations in France and Belgium, e.g. "Collinear couples: (a,b) is equipollent to (c,d) if and only if there is a couple (x,y) not collinear with (a,b) such that (a,b) is equipollent to (x,y) and (x,y) is equipollent to (c,d)" (from Lower course Intermediate Certificate syllabus). From 1987, new syllabuses were introduced which show a marked difference in approach. The revised syllabuses are at three levels, A, B,and C; syllabus A being intended for the more able pupils. (In the first set of examinations students divided between the three syllabuses in the rough proportions 2 : 3 : 1. However, as happens in England, there was evidence that students were sometimes taught a syllabus "above" that for which they were examined.) Each syllabus is divided into three sections – a section being approximately one year's work, "depending on the particular circumstances of the class".

Although history of mathematics is not included in the syllabus, teachers are specifically asked to refer to it, where appropriate, and to the lives of great mathematicians.

The syllabuses for the various courses are indicated below – the courses for which a topic is included in the syllabus is shown following the topic or group of topics. It is to be understood that depth of treatment will vary with the course. Some schools start by teaching a common course, roughly corresponding to Syllabus B, and then differentiate later. Others stream and provide two or three courses from the start.

The three types of school (see the "structure diagram") all offer the main mathematics courses.

Section One, Intermediate Certificate (i.e. roughly Grade 8, age 12–13).

Sets: Listing of elements (A,B,C), membership defined by a rule (A,B), subsets, universe, complement, empty set, equality of sets, Venn diagrams (A,B,C), intersection and union of sets (A, two sets only B, C), commutativity (A,B,C), difference (A).

Relations and functions: Couples, use of arrow diagrams (A,B,C: simple relations only for C), domain, codomain, range, function as a special kind of relation (A).

Natural numbers: Naturals, place value (A,B,C), sets of divisors, pairs of factors, prime numbers (A,B), sets of multiples, lcm (A,B,C), cardinal number of set (A,B), four operations (A,B, division without remainders C), approximate answers, commutativity, powers with natural exponents (A,B,C), rules for indices (A).

Integers: Set of integers, addition, number line and order (A,B,C), four operations (A,B), arrow diagrams to illustrate relations, intervals (A,B).

Rationals: Set of rationals (A,B, positive rationals with emphasis on those having 2, 3, 4, 7, 8, 16, 5, 10, 100, 1000 as denominator (C)), equivalent fractions, four operations (A,B, restricted to positive rationals (C)), approximate answers (A,B,C), fractions as decimals (A,B, only terminating (C)), ratio and proportion (A,B), decimals and fractions on number line (A,B).

Reals: Every point on number line corresponds to a real, linear inequalities in one variable and graphing solution set on number line (A,B).

Measure: SI units of length, area, time, mass (A,B,C), multiples and submultiples, area (square, rectangle), volume (cuboids), square root (A,B).

Money: Shopping bills (C), profit and loss, percentage discount, percentage profit, bills, rates, tax, annual interest, value added tax (A,B).

Algebraic expressions: Variable, constant, term, expression, coefficient, evaluation, addition and subtraction of simple algebraic expressions (distributive property and the removal of brackets, multiplication of simple expressions and division by factors (A)).

Equations: First degree equations in one variable (A,B).

Tables: Use of square, square root and reciprocal tables.

Geometry: This differs markedly between the three levels:

A: Congruence conditions for triangles assumed, theorems on angles, eg vertically opposite, angle sum, external angle of triangle, opposite angles and sides of parallelogram, base angles of isosceles triangle.

B: Use of ruler, compasses, set squares, protractor to construct squares, rectangles, and triangles; angle sum, simple properties of square, rectangle, parallelogram, construction of parallelograms given various pieces of data.

C: Use of ruler, compasses, protractor, set squares; measurement of line segments, area of square or rectangle, perimeter of same, construction of squares and rectangles.

Section Two, Intermediate Certificate (i.e. roughly Grade 9, age 13–14):

A Course:

Symmetric difference, associativity, need for brackets, closure under an operation, cartesian product, composition, inverse of functions, coordinates in plane, graphing linear and quadratic functions.
First degree equations in two variables, problems, solutions, graphs.
Rationals as decimals, terminating and periodic decimals as fractions.
Scientific notation.
Compound interest.
Perimeter and area of circle, surface areas and volumes of cylinder, cone, sphere.

Pythagoras and applications.
Cos, sine, tan, values (where defined) for 0, 30, 45, 60, 90, 180, 270, 360 degrees.
Factors of $6xy + 3y^2$, $ax^2 + bx + c$, $x^2 - 4y^2$, $x^3 - y^3$, $x^3 + y^3$ etc.
Solution of quadratics by factorisation.
Bar and pie charts, trend graphs, histograms, frequency tables, mean and mode, cumulative frequency, ogive, median, interquartile range, mean of group frequency distribution.
Construction of mid–points and perpendicular bisectors.
Symmetry in lines and points, translations, parallel projections, images of points (using coordinates) under these, rotation (as combination of two reflections), use of set squares and compasses to verify, eg two reflections in parallel lines give a translation, two point–reflections give a translation.
Theorems on perpendicular bisectors, angle bisectors, angle at circumference is twice ..., perpendicularity of tangent to a circle.

B Course:

Difference, complement, set operations for three sets, domain, range, function as a relation.
Distributive property for removing brackets, multiplication and factorisation of algebraic expressions, quadratic equations by factorisation.
Bar charts, pie charts, trend graphs.
Scientific notation, use of square, square root and reciprocal tables, radius, diameter, chord of circle, pi, circumference and area of circle.
Translations (use of equipollent couples), angle theorems for parallel lines (assumed), SAS rule for congruence, theorems on angles in parallelogram, triangles, angle in semi–circle, construction of angle bisector.

C Course:

Place value for decimals, addition,subtraction and multiplication of decimals, rounding off (not more than three decimal places), approximating.
Fraction to percentage, easy fractions and decimals as percentages, equivalence of fractions, decimals and percentages.
Percentage discount, calculations on profit and loss etc.
Bar and pie charts, trend graphs.
Constructions in the plane, verification (by measurement) of angle sum and Pythagoras, and, by paper cutting or otherwise, that area of a triangle is half base times height.
Volume of rectangular solids.
Speed.

Evaluating simple algebraic expressions, linear equations in one variable with a whole number solution.

Section Three, Intermediate Certificate (i.e. roughly Grade 10, age 14–15):

A Course:

Max and min of quadratic functions found graphically, graphical solution of quadratic inequalities, formula for solution of quadratic equations.
Rearrangement of algebraic formulae, addition and subtraction of simple linear rational expressions.
Logs to different bases and usual rules, arithmetical operations with surds.
Trigonometric functions for right angled triangle, area of triangle, sine rule.
Slope of line in coordinates, $y = mx + c$, parallel and perpendicular lines, intersection of lines, image of line under translation.
Dividing a line segment into a given number of parts of equal length (construction with proof).
Thales' theorem for triangles, properties of similar triangles, intersecting chord and tangent theorems, Pythagoras.

B Course:

Coordinating the plane, drawing linear graphs, first degree equations in two variables, problems, solutions and graphical treatment.
Distance formula, slope, mid–point formula, forms for equation of a straight line.
Compound interest (formula not required).
Use of formulae for surface area and volume of a cylinder and sphere.
Expressing data (discrete) as frequency table, mean and mode.
Graphical illustration and interpretation of quadratic functions.
Factorisation of simple quadratics (leading coefficient prime) and difference of two squares. Solution of quadratics (formula optional), applications.
Addition and subtraction of expressions of form $1/(x+a)$, equations of the form $1/(x-1) - (1/x) = 1/2$, manipulation of formulae.
Sine, cosine and tangent, tables, right–angled triangle problems (congruence properties assumed).
Theorems on parallelogram, trisection of a given line segment, area of parallelogram and triangle, symmetry theorems and constructions.
Note: proofs of theorems are not examined in the B Course.

C Course:

Compound interest (not more than three years), income tax, bills, VAT, meter readings, different types of charges.
Discrete data arranged in frequency table, mean and mode.
Evaluating quadratic expressions.
Use of square root and square tables.
Distance from a map, drawing to scale.
Plotting points having integral coordinates, joining points to form a line, drawing, say, $y = 3x + 5$.
Idea of parallel and perpendicular lines, constructions using set squares, bisection of angle, dividing a line segment into two or more equal parts.
Radius, diameter, chord of circle, pi, circumference formula, verification by measurement of right angle and cyclic quadrilateral properties, construction of tangents, inscribed and circumscribed squares and their areas.
Volume of a cylinder.
Use of instruments to construct images under line and point symmetries.

Leaving Certificate Programme

The Leaving Certificate Programme in Irish schools is relatively unspecialised: pupils typically take seven subjects. Although Mathematics is not compulsory, it is taken by most students. Important changes are taking place to the mathematics syllabuses at this level. The 1990 intake to the senior cycle is being offered three Leaving Certificate courses: Higher, Ordinary and Ordinary Alternative. (These roughly correspond to the A, B and C courses of the junior cycle.) The Ordinary Alternative course is an interim one. Revised versions of the other two courses leading to the Leaving Certificate will shortly appear in a new format. At present they are presented as examination syllabuses with a short preamble setting out general objectives, eg the teacher should:

> present mathematics as an ever–expanding, open–ended subject;
> show mathematics both as an abstract, autonomous body of knowledge and as a useful operational tool.

Higher Course

Complex numbers: need, conjugate, modulus, Argand diagram, meaning of mod(z–a), easy loci, complex roots of polynomials with real coefficients, de Moivre (proof by induction for naturals, applications for rationals), properties of modulus of products, inequalities for mod(z+w) and mod(z–w).

Equations: linear equations and inequalities in two variables, sets of linear equations in three variables, use of remainder theorem to find roots of cubics, approximate roots of cubics.

Binomial Theorem: permutations and combinations, proof by induction for n natural, applications for n rational.

Line and circle: distance, angle between lines, parametric equation of line, equation of line through point of intersection of two lines, equation of pair of lines in (ax + by + c)(dx + ey + f) = 0 form, general equation of circle, circle through points of intersection of (i) two circles, (ii) line and circle, equation of tangent at a point on circle, intersection of line and circle.

Trigonometry: derivation and application of standard formulae, domain, codomain and range of trig functions, periodicity, inverse functions.

Matrices: 2x2, addition and multiplication by a scalar, product, inverse, applications to linear transformations.

Either Statistics **or** Vectors and linear transformations

Statistics: sample point and space, event, mutually exclusive events, probability axioms, equally likely, conditional, independent, binomial distribution, mean, variance (no proof required for variance), standard units, use of tables to test a null hypothesis.

Vectors and linear transformations: vector representing translation, pointed plane, addition, scalar multiplication, commutativity and distributivity, length of a vector, transformation of the plane as a map, linear transformation defined by f(ax + by)= af(**x**) + bf(**y**), orthonormal basis, scalar product and geometrical meaning, parallel projection on a line through origin is a linear transformation, scalar product distributes addition, coordinate form of scalar product, parametric vector equation of line, point dividing line segment in a given ratio, centroid of triangle, collinearity of circumcentre, orthocentre and centroid.

Either the Parabola **or** Groups

Parabola: as a locus, canonical equations, parametric equations, tangent to a parabola, general equation of a parabola.

Groups: definition, Abelian, examples from numbers, matrices, residue classes, symmetries of equilateral triangle and square, set of subsets and symmetric difference, recognition of subgroups, isomorphism of two groups.

Sequences and series: simple limits assuming theorems on sums, products and quotients, arithmetic and geometric sequences, repayment of loans, compound interest, convergence and divergence of sequences, series including arithmetic and geometric, convergence and divergence of series, comparison and ratio tests for series of positive terms.

Calculus: derivatives from first principles, rate of change, products, quotients, composite, polynomials, max and min, points of inflection, curve sketching, (including ellipse and parabola), trig and inverse trig (arcsin, arctan), exponential, logarithmic, parametric ($x = f(t)$, $y = g(t)$); integration of x^r and polynomials, trigonometric functions (including $\sin^2$, $\sin^3$, $\sin mx \cos^2 mx$), exponential functions, product of sines and cosines of multiplc angles, substitutions (and integrals producing inverse trig functions), definite integrals, areas and volumes of revolution.

Ordinary Course

Mensuration of regular areas and solids including cone.
Frequency, cumulative frequency, graphical treatment, median, standard deviation (without use of assumed mean), weighted averages.
Solution of quadratics and cubics with at least one integral root, linear equations and sets of equations in two or three unknowns, including cases with non–unique solutions, equations involving rational expressions leading to quadratics, manipulation of formulae.
Using remainder theorem to factorise simple cubics.
Simple applications of indices.
APs and GPs, derivation of formulae, summation, compound interest, sum of infinite GP.
Examples of order relations, domain, codomain, range, bijections, inverse functions, composition of functions.
Graphs of quadratics and cubics, interpretation of changes of value and sign.
Quadratic inequalities in one variable, linear inequalities in two variables and elementary linear programming.

Radian measure, sine and cosine functions for all angles, periodicity, tangent, compound angle formulae, simple identities, area of triangle, sine and cosine rules with applications.
Complex numbers, four operations, Argand diagram, modulus.
Concurrency results for triangle, centroid, orthocentre, circle angle theorems, area theorems for triangles, Thales for triangle, chord and tangent theorems for circle, Pythagoras.
Coordinates, distance, area of triangle, midpoint of segment, slope, equation of straight line, line through given points, through a point parallel or perpendicular to a given line, intersection of two lines, equation of circle, intersection of line and circle, tangent to circle.
Composition of two translations, vectors, addition, subtraction and scalar multiplication, pointed plane, perpendicular unit vectors.
Binomial Theorem, factorial and r from n notations, easy applications (no proofs required).
Rate of change, tangent line, slope, derivative as a limit, derivatives of polynomials of degree less than four, x^n, sum, product, quotient and chain rules, simple applications, graph drawing, max and min.

Ordinary Level - Alternative

Many students who took syllabus C in the Intermediate certificate now remain in school beyond the years of compulsory education. In order to cater for their needs, a new "Alternative" Leaving Certificate syllabus has been devised.

The course makes considerable use of the calculator and, in general, encourages an exploratory and reflective approach to learning. It is much influenced by the findings of the Cockcroft Committee (*Mathematics Counts,* HMSO, London, 1982).

Although parts of the course revise work covered in the lower secondary school, it is intended that these should now be treated differently. Syllabus content is (briefly) as follows:

Number systems: revision of naturals, integers, rationals and reals, the four operations, the number line, inequalities, decimals, powers and roots, scientific notation. Factors, multiples, primes, Prime factor theorem. Use of brackets, conventions, easy algebraic manipulation of formulae and solution of equations.

Arithmetic: approximation and error, rounding off, relative error, percentage error, tolerance, very large and very small numbers on the calculator, limits to accuracy of calculators. Substitution in formulae. Proportion, percentage, averages, average rates of change with respect to time. Compound interest formulae. VAT, rates, income tax, tax tables. Domestic finance and budgets, bills. Currency transactions, commission. Costing, materials and labour. Metric and Imperial systems, conversion.

Areas and volumes: plane figures – disc, rectangle, triangle, parallelogram, trapezium. Solids – right cone, cuboid, cylinder, sphere, right prism. Simpson's rule to approximate area.

Algebra: linear equations with decimal coefficients, two simultaneous linear equations in two unknowns with integer coefficients. Simple quadratics with real solutions.

Statistics and probability: multiplicative principle of counting, discrete probability, relative frequency and equally–likely outcome. Graphical and tabular representation of data, grouped and ungrouped frequency distributions, mean, cumulative frequencies and graph, median, weighted mean. Concept of dispersion, standard deviation (not more than ten numbers).

Trigonometry: Sine, cosine and tangent as ratios in a right–angled triangle, solving for one unknown in a right–angled triangle.

Functions and graphs: function as a set of couples and as a formula or rule, linear and quadratic functions, experimental fitting of straight lines, periodic functions (informally), interpretation of graphs, distance/time, speed/time, depth of liquid/time, conversion of units.

Geometry: coordinate geometry, distance between points, slope of lines, parallel and perpendicular lines, midpoint of line segment, $y = mx + c$, finding equation of line. Knowledge of standard geometric results (no proofs) on angles and lines (corresponding, alternate, etc), parallelograms, angle sums, Pythagoras. Constructions using ruler and compasses – perpendiculars, angles equal to given angle, parallelogram, circumscribed and inscribed circles of a triangle, tangent to a circle. Enlargement of rectilinear figure by rays, centre of enlargement, scale factor, finding centre of enlargement, scale factor and area. Nets of rectangular solids, pyramids and right prisms with triangular cross–section. Repeating patterns, axial symmetry, planes of symmetry, central and rotational symmetry in given figures.

Investigations: development of concepts and strategies for investigating mathematical problems and observing general patterns and results.

ITALY

Age (yr)	Grade				
5-6	K	Nursery School			
6-7	1	Primary (Elementary) School			
7-8	2				
8-9	3				
9-10	4				
10-11	5				
11-12	6	Middle School			
12-13	7				
13-14	8				
14-15	9	Lyceum	Technical	Vocational	Primary Teacher Training
15-16	10				
16-17	11				
17-18	12				
18-19	13				

Notes

1. Nursery school (3–6) is not compulsory, but 75% of 3 year–olds and almost 90% of 5 year–olds attend such schools.

2. About 60% of the cohort stay on at school post 14. Some 27% of these attend Lyceums, 46% Technical Schools, 20% Vocational Institutes (some for only two or three years), and 7% train to be elementary school teachers (4 year course).

3. Promotion of students is not automatic at the end of the year, but is based on assessment of progress. This is done internally except at the ends of Grades 5 and 8 and of Grade 13 (the Ministerially–directed "Maturitá" examination). In the middle schools retention rates are about 10%. In the secondary schools about 20% of pupils are required to retake examinations in September.

4. All successful Grade 13 leavers from the Lyceums and Technical Institutes automatically qualify for university entrance.

ITALY

A National Curriculum is never to be taken as a factual statement of what is actually taught in schools. In every country individual teachers will add, omit or alter the emphasis. This is perhaps particularly true of Italy where the system is not so controlled by external examinations as is the case in other countries. Nevertheless, a national curriculum is a public statement which explicitly displays a view of mathematics, of how it should be taught, on what is desirable, and what is thought possible. As such it has considerable interest by itself. Yet mathematics is only one of a number of subjects and its teaching is very much influenced by the overall construction of the curriculum. This must be borne very much in mind in the case of Italy, for there the general curriculum for Grades 9–13, with its allocation of hours, has remained unchanged for almost seventy years. As a result even students in the Scientific Lyceum still spend four hours a week on Latin as opposed to three hours on mathematics. Such a time allocation is a severe constraint on curriculum development.

Yet the general lack of uniformity within the Italian system has permitted and encouraged much experimentation by a band of committed teachers. It is, perhaps, their aspirations for all which are reflected in the current national syllabuses.

The Italian syllabus for compulsory education (ie ages 6–14) is essentially divided into three stages ending respectively at 8, 11 and 14. Syllabuses are laid down for individual stages and not for individual years. A teacher is free to order material within any stage. (It is, however, intended that the same teacher should teach the class throughout each stage.) There are no indications of how time should be distributed within the curriculum. Indeed, the observations on the 'syllabus' and the guidance provided on how it should be interpreted effectively exclude such advice for they indicate how certain objectives, eg the development of the concepts of relations, functions and correspondences (Theme 7 of the 11–14 stage), must be gradual over the three years whenever opportunities present themselves. Teachers are, however, recommended to deal with the most difficult topics on more than one occasion: each time treating the topic in greater depth. In general, assessment is based not on attainment in standard, written tests, but rather on oral exposition by the pupil and achievement in written exercises and work throughout the year.

Nursery education (3–6)

National syllabuses exist for the state schools but these give no particular attention to mathematics.

Primary school (6–11)

The emphasis throughout the first (6–8) and second (8–11) stages is on a propaedeutical approach without undue formalisation. Teachers at this level are 'class teachers' and not mathematics specialists. They will often have care of a class throughout the whole 5 years of primary school. However, it is planned that in future there will be three teachers at each of the two primary stages (thus building in additional support at the 'infant' stage): one of whom should have some specialisation in science and mathematics.

The 1985 syllabus divides mathematics into five themes: problems; arithmetic; geometry and measure; logic; probability, statistics and computer science.

1. **Problems** is seen to concern a general methodology of teaching (teaching by means of problems), which it is argued ought to be characteristic of mathematics teaching at all times. Here 'problem' is taken to mean an open problematic situation arising from experience or school work, rather than a 'routine exercise'. General objectives are set out for this theme, eg 'translating an elementary problem expressed in words into a mathematical form, operating on this, finding a solution, and correctly interpreting the result'. However, no attempt is made to assign such objectives to individual stages. Rather, these objectives are seen as universal ones, appropriate (at different levels of sophistication) at all stages of mathematics teaching.

2. **Arithmetic** comprises much that is standard and traditional: naturals, fractions, decimals, the integers and the number line. (Ratio, percentage and proportion are considered in the 11–14 stage.) Again there is no attempt to sub-divide the learning process by putting strict bounds on which numbers should be covered in any one year.

First stage (6–8) (summary)

counting – forwards and backwards; associating various activities with this sequence of words;
associating a number with a group of objects and developing the concept of conservation;
reading and writing the natural numbers up to 100 in words and symbols; using the symbols $=$, $<$, $>$ and the number line;
mental addition and subtraction;
partitioning objects into pairs, triples,... as a foundation for division and multiplication;

using objects, learn to calculate twice/half, three times/ a third,...
using numbers up to at least one hundred, learn how to add, subtract, multiply and divide (the last two with one digit numbers).

Second stage (8–11)

read numbers, natural and decimal, express them in symbols and words, and see them as a sum of thousands, hundreds, tens, units, tenths, hundredths, etc;
write these numbers in symbols or words, understand place value, the significance of the use of zero and of the decimal point;
represent and order these numbers on the number line;
write out a sequence given a rule and suggest a rule for a given sequence;
understand and use the commutative and associative laws for addition and multiplication, the distributive law, the inverse properties of subtraction and division, and use appropriate strategies and approximations to carry out mental calculations;
understand the four operations on naturals and decimals and the significance of algorithms for calculating;
multiply and divide by ten, hundred, thousand and understand the significance of these operations;
prime numbers;
find the fraction representing part of a geometric figure, set of objects, etc. and, vice versa, given a fraction shade in an appropriate part,... . (particular attention to decimal subdivision);
represent and order simple fractions on the number line;
represent and order integers on the number line (building on experiences such as a thermometer);
learn and use conventions for the order of operations and for brackets.

3. **Geometry and measure** primarily aims to provide a progressive organisation of spatial knowledge and the introduction of a system of reference. Particular attention is given to the 'correct acquisition of the fundamental concepts of length, area, volume, angle, parallelism and perpendicularity'.

The need to coordinate the teaching of measure in mathematics and in science is stressed.

First stage

use of words such as before/behind, over/under, right/left,...;
gain an idea of length in relation to say height, learn to talk and write about the concept and use simple graphical representation;

distinguish between plane and solid;
recognise symmetry;
measure lengths, capacity, time using appropriate units (arbitrary or conventional) and suitable subdivisions

Second stage

learn to recognise, describe and construct the principal plane figures and also simple solid ones: learn to characterise them by, say, numbers of vertices, edges, faces;
preservation of area under decomposition and reconstitution;
measure and calculate areas and perimeters of the principal plane figures and learn to distinguish between the notions of area and perimeter;
find the volumes of irregular objects by various strategies, distinguish between the notions of volume and surface area;
indicate positions in the plane by various means (direction, distance, angle, coordinate grid); use correctly expressions such as, vertical, horizontal, parallel line, incident, perpendicular; draw using ruler, compasses and protractor, parallels, perpendiculars, angles, polygons;
recognise symmetry and classify triangles and quadrilaterals by their symmetries;
study, making use of concrete materials and drawings, axial symmetry, translations, rotations and enlargements.
know and use the principal international units of length, area, volume/capacity, weight;
use instruments for measuring;
translate from one kind of common measure to another;
measure of angles (degrees), time (hours, minutes, seconds).

4. **Logic** is not to be taught in a formal manner, but is to be developed gradually. Particular care is devoted to using **normal** language precisely. Ideas which are suggested for development include problems of classification, the use of graphs and diagrams, an introduction to the language of set theory.

First stage

classification of objects, figures,... by attribute;
representation (for example, by arrows) of successive events in time, relationships of order, correspondences,... with reference to concrete situations;

Second stage

classification and representation using, eg Venn diagrams, tables;

the use of language of sets (union, intersection, complementary) and of logical connectives.

5. **Probability, statistics and computer studies** are again treated in an informal fashion. It is stressed that the classical definition of probability should not be the point of departure, but rather the point of arrival.

First stage

to use sensibly in situations taken from real life and games such expressions as: perhaps, it's possible, it's certain, it can't be, it's impossible.

Second stage

to carry out observations, collect and display data using bar charts, histograms,..., to calculate the mean (using pocket calculators if possible);
to interpret tables and diagrams;
to meet probability of events in a variety of games (cards, dice, ...);
to list (graphically or otherwise) all possible cases in simple combinatorial situations and make some elementary estimates of probability;
to construct and interpret simple and appropriate flow diagrams (hands-on experience with a computer is not assumed).

Teachers are expected to interpret the syllabus and accompanying methodological instructions and to fill in the finer details for themselves. Teachers are responsible for fixing assessment criteria for both the annual assessment procedures (normally continuous throughout the year) and the examination at the end of elementary school.

The Middle School (11–14)

The number of hours for mathematics and science per week, 6 in total out of 30, is fixed nationally. It is recommended that three of these are devoted to mathematics teaching. (The same teacher teaches mathematics **and** science and will usually teach throughout the three grades.) Again, examination regulations are laid down centrally, but individual teachers can determine assessment criteria.

The syllabus, dating from 1979, is very concise but is accompanied by statements of objectives, suggestions on methodology, and more general observations on how the 'letter' of the syllabus might be interpreted.

There are seven 'themes':

1. Geometry – a first representation of the physical world

(a) geometrical objects and concepts: a study of figures in the plane and space;
(b) length, area, volumes, angles and their measure;
(c) simple isoperimetric and equi–areal problems – Pythagoras' Theorem;
(d) geometric constructions (ruler, compasses, protractor).

2. Numbers

(a) natural numbers, extension to integers; fractions (as operators) to rationals; ratio, percentage, proportion; number line;
(b) decimal notation; orders of magnitude;
(c) operations and inverses on various sets of numbers; powers and roots; multiples and divisors; lcm and gcd; decomposition into prime factors; exercises in calculation – exact and approximate; repeated approximations to a real number; use of calculating aids – tables, pocket calculators, etc.

3. Mathematics of the certain and the probable

(a) differences between true/false and probabilistic situations; correct use of logical connectives (and, or, not), their interpretation as operations on sets and applications to electric circuits;
(b) the collection of statistics and their graphical representation (histograms, pie charts, ...); frequency, mean;
(c) notions of probability and its applications;

4. Problems and equations

(a) identification of significant data and variables in a problem; resolution by means of a variety of procedures (flow diagram, translation into arithmetical expressions,...);
(b) the use of letters and the transposition of simple formulae;
(c) simple linear equations and inequalities;

5. Coordinate methods

(a) use of coordinates in everyday situations, maps and grids;
(b) coordinates of a point on a line, in a plane; representation and study of simple plane figures, eg polygons given by the coordinates of their vertices;

(c) simple mathematical laws relating also to the physical world, economics, etc, and their representation in the cartesian plane; direct and inverse proportionality, quadratic functions, etc.

6. Transformation geometry

(a) plane isometries; their composition; direct and indirect congruence;
(b) similarities in the plane, in particular, enlargements; scale;
(c) observations on other geometric transformations (shadows, photographs,...), deformed shapes.

7. Structures and structural analogies

Concepts of relations, correspondence, function; rules of composition in various contexts; searching for and discovering similarities in structure.

Secondary Education

Secondary school commences at 14+. Traditionally the path to university was through the Lyceum of which there are four types (Classical, Scientific, Linguistic and Artistic). Now the Technical Institutes provide a second path. About one quarter of students attend further forms of secondary education: vocational institutes and institutes for training elementary school teachers.

Briefly the various mathematics syllabuses are:

Classical (2 hours per week, 3 in year 3)

Elementary algebra, Euclidean geometry, proportionality, the reals, and trigonometry (in the final year).

Scientific (5, 4, 3, 3, 3 hours per week respectively in the five years)

Classical syllabus in greater depth plus elementary analytical geometry and differential and integral calculus. (No probability or statistics.)

Artistic and Linguistic

Watered–down version of the Classical Lyceum syllabus.

Teachers' Institute (4 years)

Classical syllabus (without the final year's trigonometry) with less emphasis on algebra and more attention paid to arithmetic and its teaching.

Technical Institutes

The hours per week and syllabuses vary according to speciality of which the institutions offer a very varied selection. The calculus is taught in some institutes as are combinatorics, statistics and probability. There is also some hands-on computer work.

Vocational institutes

Varied syllabuses but usually weak.

The new, common syllabus

It is hoped/intended shortly to introduce common syllabuses in the first two years (14–16) of all secondary schools. Mathematics will then be offered at two levels A (higher) and B (lower). At the present time about 30% of schools are using these syllabuses as an 'experiment'.

Again the bare bones of a 'stage' syllabus are presented (on this occasion split into five themes) together with observations concerning objectives and methodology. Thus the process objectives are given due weight in the accompanying notes.

We give below the syllabus for the A course (5 hours per week). The material contained in the square brackets is omitted from the B course. (It is not assumed that there will be identical treatments of the shared content.)

1. Elements of logic and computer science

(a) Propositions, logical connectives (not, and, or, implies, is implied by, is equivalent to); truth tables and tautologies; *modus ponens, modus tollens* and other deductive procedures;
(b) variables, predicates, quantifiers;
[(c) algorithms, their construction and representation;]
(d) a first introduction to formal language;

(e) laboratory work on computers : operations, languages of command and of programming; use of a programming language; consideration of errors; syntax and semantics; practical experience in various contexts.

2. The geometry of the plane and of space

(a) The [Cartesian] plane: incidence, parallelism, orthogonality;
(b) isometries and their composition;
(c) plane figures and their properties, polygons, Pythagoras;
(d) symmetry, in particular, in 3–D;
[(e) homotheties and similarities in the plane; Thales;]
(f) Cartesian equations of line [, parabola, circle];
[(g) cosine and sine and the sine and cosine rules;]
[(h) elementary transformations in 3–D];

3. Number sets and calculations

(a) Operations on finite sets and the first notions of combinatorics;
(b) operations on and ordering of rationals;
(c) approximations and their use in elementary calculations; the significance of digits, intuitive introduction to the reals; [square roots of the positive reals and elementary operations on them;]
(d) the language of algebra and calculations 'with letters';

4. Relations and functions

(a) Cartesian product; order and equivalence relations; functions and their composition;
(b) linear [and quadratic] functions; [$x \rightarrow k/x$;] linear [and quadratic] equations and inequalities; systems of equations;

5. Elements of probability and statistics

(a) simple probability spaces; random events; mutually exclusive events and the 'rule of sums';
(b) conditional probability and applications; [Bayes' theorem;]
(c) elements of descriptive statistics; collection of data; indices of variability, regression and correlation.

JAPAN

Age (yr)	Grade	
5-6	K	Kindergarten
6-7	1	Elementary School
7-8	2	
8-9	3	
9-10	4	
10-11	5	
11-12	6	
12-13	7	Lower Secondary School
13-14	8	
14-15	9	
15-16	10	Upper Secondary School
16-17	11	
17-18	12	

Notes

1. Kindergarten commences at age 3. About two–thirds of all 5 year–olds attend. Almost all other 5 year–olds attend day nurseries.

2. Upper secondary school, which is not compulsory, is attended by over 94% of the age cohort. A small number of these study part–time.

JAPAN

The presence of Japan in a 'medal' position in any international study of pupils' attainment and its rapid progress as a leading economic and industrial power makes the study of its curriculum particularly interesting.

We refer elsewhere to the way in which the educational systems of, say, the Netherlands and West Germany are distinguished by the degree of differentiation built into them. Japan, on the other hand, has a system of remarkable uniformity. There is no differentiation of mathematics syllabuses until the age of 15. Neither is it the case that repetition of years is common. Japanese society is noted for its homogeneity (although there are signs that this is weakening) and differentiation militates against this. Yet homogeneity demands sacrifices from the able, who may be left unchallenged, and from the below average, who will have to struggle hard to keep up with their classmates. This latter 'struggle' leads many to attend the *juku*, private educational establishments, operating in the evenings and weekends, which supplement day–time school attendance. Japanese pupils are **expected** to achieve both by parents and teachers.

The first external examination is that taken at 15+. This takes two distinct forms. The private, upper–secondary schools set their own entrance examinations, which are very severe in the case of the famous ones. Public examinations are set by the various Provincial Prefectures. Thus, although, syllabuses at the 15–18 level are not differentiated, the schools which pupils attend are. In particular, the 'technical' schools (attended by a small minority of pupils) follow the syllabuses only in a nominal fashion. It is usual for pupils to attempt the entrance examinations of various schools (and often to call on the aid of the *juku* in preparing for them). Pupils who fail an examination can resit later that year.

The examinations at 18+ are set by (in general, individual) institutions of higher and further education.

As will be seen, the Japanese syllabuses have recently been revised. Implementation is delayed until textbooks can be prepared. Various series are available, usually written by teams of school teachers, mathematics educators, mathematicians and professional editors. All texts have to be approved by the Ministry.

Kindergarten (ages 3–6) (effective 1990 on)

The years of Kindergarten are not compulsory: it can be entered at any age between 3 and 5. Objectives and content are set out under three headings: health, human relations, environment and language. That children should develop an interest in numbers, quantities and geometrical figures in their daily lives is one of the aims of the third domain, ie environment.

Elementary School (ages 6–12) (effective 1992 on)

Mathematics (or, as the syllabus puts it, arithmetic) is compulsory in all grades: the standard number of 45 minute periods per year devoted to it being 1st Grade 136, succeeding grades 175.

The syllabus is presented in the form of 'objectives' for the whole six years ("to help children develop their abilities to consider their daily–life phenomena insightfully and logically, acquire the fundamental knowledge and skills regarding numbers, quantities and geometrical figures, and thereby to foster their attitude to appreciate mathematics, and to cope with it and willingly make use of it in their lives") followed by an individual 'grade' breakdown of objectives and contents. There then follow brief remarks concerning content (eg if the object is to assure the understanding of 2–digit numbers then some allusions must be made to 3–digit ones). We here summarise only the entries under 'content', making reference, where appropriate, to relevant 'remarks'.

Grade 1 (6–7)

Number and calculations: matching, counting, representing, ordering, decomposing, place value for 2–digit numbers, addition and subtraction, when applicable, 1–digit additions and subtraction as inverse, simple preliminary 2–digit work, dividing objects into groups of equal number.

Quantities and measurement: comparison of length, area, volume, use of ad hoc units, reading a clock.

Geometrical figures: recognising, constructing and decomposing shapes; 'front' and 'back', 'right' and 'left', 'up' and 'down'.

Grade 2 (7–8)

Numbers and calculations: deepening understanding and widening experience; place value up to 4 digits, simple classification, relation between addition and subtraction, extending 1–digit operations to 2 and 3 digit numbers, devising algorithms for addition and subtraction, why multiplication, commutativity of multiplication, construction of tables, knowledge of tables for 1–digit numbers, use of equality and inequality signs.

Quantities and measurement: work directed towards an understanding of length and volume, meaning and use of standard units, mm, cm, m, ml, dl, l, relations of day, hour and minutes.

Geometrical figures: shapes through concrete manipulation, triangles and quadrilaterals, recognising, making and drawing squares, rectangles and right–angled triangles (understanding through tessellations, **not** tessellations as curriculum content)

Grade 3 (8–9)

Numbers and calculations: place of ten thousands (Japanese unit), sizes of 10 times, 100 times, $^{1}/_{10}$ of whole numbers and representation, relative size of numbers; addition and subtraction, checking computations, multiplication of 2– and 3–digit numbers by 1– and 2–digit numbers by extension of previous results, column form of multiplication (long), commutative and associative laws and use in checking; why and when division, relation between division and multiplication, remainders, column form of division by 1–digit divisor; decimal and vulgar fractions to represent fractional parts induced by equal sharing, to know that decimals and fractions can be added and subtracted; simple addition and subtraction on the Japanese abacus (soroban), simple mental arithmetic.

Quantities and measurements: concept of weight, g and kg, length, appropriate units, km, estimation of length, deepening of concept of time, calculations on time.

Geometrical figures: patterns using ruler and compasses, isosceles and equilateral triangles, angles in relation to fundamental geometrical figures, centre, diameter and radius of a circle, circles and spheres.
Quantitative relations: representing a relation by a formula, use of frames and investigating values which lead to true statements; simple tables and graphs, including bar graphs; reading scales graduated by 2, 5, 20, 50 etc.

Grade 4 (9–10)

Numbers and calculations: revising and summarising decimal system, rounding, further practice in multiplication, exploring the relation

dividend = divisor x quotient + remainder,

deepening understanding of decimals and fractions, addition and subtraction of decimals, algorithms for multiplication and division by whole numbers, deepening understanding of fractions, addition of fractions with a common denominator, revision and fuller comprehension of the four operations and an understanding of the commutative, associative and distributive laws, addition and subtraction on the soroban.

Quantities and measurements: concept and measurement of area, cm^2, m^2, km^2, a, ha, area of squares and rectangles; concept and measurement of angles, degree, half–turn, full–turn.

Geometrical figures: basic plane shapes, parallelism, perpendicularity, parallelograms, trapeziums, rhombuses; basic solids, cubes, cuboids, parallelism and perpendicularity in connection with cuboid, beginning to appreciate how solids are represented by diagrams in the plane; first ideas on representing position of a point in space.

Quantitative relations: first concepts of functional relationships – how two quantities vary together, graphs, brackets and operations, use of formula, variable values represented by frames; gathering, classifying and arranging data, graphs.

Grade 5 (10–11)

Numbers and calculations: odd and even numbers, divisors and multiples, multiplication by 10, 100, $^1/_{10}$, $^1/_{100}$; multiplication and division of decimals, transforming fractions into decimals, equivalent fractions, comparison, addition and subtraction of fractions, division of two whole numbers yields a fraction, estimation by rounding.

Quantities and measurements: areas of triangles, parallelograms, trapezia, polygons (by decomposition), circle; concept and measurement of volume, cm^3, m^3, volume of cube and cuboid; estimation of quantities by rough measurement (length, area, volume), use of 'average', idea of ratio, per unit, concept and calculation of speed.

Geometrical figures: observation and construction of basic figures, congruent figures and their shared properties, shape and size as distinct factors, ratio of circumference of circle to diameter, drawing regular n–gons and investigating properties using circles.

Quantitative relations: percentage (including special Japanese role of '10 per cent'), deepening understanding of relations between two quantities, formulae, use of letters instead of frames, classification and arrangement of data, pie charts and bar graphs.

Grade 6 (11–12)

Numbers and calculations: deepening of understanding of multiplication and division, multiplication and division of fractions, applications, division as multiplication by reciprocal, connecting operations on fractions with those on decimals.

Quantities and measurements: volume and surface area of basic prisms and cylinders; volume of pyramids and cones (surface area in simple cases), development of understanding of, and ability to, measure, use of proportional relationships, the metric system.

Geometrical figures: line and point symmetry, symmetries of basic figures, shape and size, scale drawings, interpreting sketch maps, plans, etc., practical work on basic solids. Quantitative relations: ratio, direct and inverse proportion, applications, use of tables and graphs to represent frequency distributions, selecting appropriate tables and graphs for given purposes, using statistical data to conjecture about tendencies.

It is expected that teachers should help children to use 'soroban' or hand–held calculators both to lighten the burden of computation and to improve the effectiveness of teaching from the fifth–grade. Such use should be complemented by work on estimation.

The Lower Secondary School (Grades 7–9, ages 12–15) (effective 1993 on)

Mathematics is a compulsory subject in each grade and an additional, optional unit may also be taken in Grade 9. The numbers of 50 minute periods allocated to compulsory mathematics are

Grade 7	105
Grade 8	140
Grade 9	140

Grade 7 (12–13)

Numbers and algebraic expressions: positive and negative numbers, the four operations, absolute value, letters as symbols, representation of multiplication and division using letters, addition and subtraction of linear expressions, linear equations in one variable – applications and solution.

Geometrical figures: basic constructions (angle bisector, perpendicular, etc.), translation, symmetry and rotation, a figure as a set of points satisfying certain conditions, developing spatial awareness, construction of solids by movement of plane figures, sections, projections and plans of solid geometrical figures (not too technical), π .

Quantitative relations: functions, variable, domain, correspondence, coordinates, tables, graphs, formulae, deepening of understanding of algebraic expressions and proportion.

Grade 8 (13–14)

Numbers and algebraic expressions, four operations on monomials, addition and subtraction of polynomials, use of algebraic expressions, transforming equalities, linear inequalities and their solution (use of flow charts), simultaneous linear equations in two variables and their solutions.

Geometrical figures: use of properties of parallel lines and congruence, properties of parallelograms and triangles, concept of similarity and properties, height, distance and similarity, properties of ratios of segments of parallel lines, applications of similarity, introduction of terms 'definition', 'proof'.

Quantitative relation: deepening of understanding of numbers and functions, binary system, standard (scientific) notation, linear functions and applications, characteristics of graphs, collection, display and interpretation of data, frequency distribution, histogram, relative frequency, mean value, range, interpretation of correlation diagrams and tables.

Grade 9 (14–15)

Numbers and algebraic expressions: square roots, expanding and factorizing simple algebraic expressions, quadratic equations, solution by factorization and by formula, rationals and irrationals, primes.

Geometrical figures: circles, circle and straight line, two circles, tangents, Pythagoras and applications, arc length, area of a sector, surface area and volume of a sphere, similarity of solids, relationships of length, area and volume in similar figures.

Quantitative relations: investigating characteristics of change, $y = ax^2$, ratio of change, stochastic events and the meaning of probability, computation of probability in simple cases (use of tree diagram), notion of estimates from a sample.

It is suggested that teachers might make passing references and introductions to work to be met in later grades and that in the 8th and 9th grades particular attention should be paid to 'problem situation' learning, ie coping with problem situations related to daily affairs. Computers and calculators should be 'efficiently utilized' in all grades, particularly when teaching 'quantitative relations'. In 'mathematics' as an optional subject (9th grade), problem situation learning, field or laboratory work, experiment and investigation should be used when appropriate 'to develop various learning activities in accord with students' characteristics'.

The Upper Secondary School (Grades 10–12, ages 15–18) (effective 1994 on)

The Upper Secondary School, although not compulsory, is attended by almost 95% of all Japanese 15 year–olds. Now mathematics is offered in a core plus options format. Thus all students must take Mathematics I, the basic foundation course; after that students select options according to their abilities and aspirations. The six courses are

Mathematics	I(4),	II(3),	III(3),
	A(2),	B(2),	C(2).

The number in brackets indicates the standard number of credits each course carries. This number multiplied by 35 gives the number of 50 minute periods allocated to each option. Mathematics I and II are seen as the common core for all those bound for higher education (roughly 35%). Mathematics III is core mathematics for those intending to specialise at university in science or mathematics. Mathematics A, B and C are options intended to provide deeper mathematical understanding and to emphasise mathematical **thought** alongside the mathematical literacy provided by the core units. It is also the case that Mathematics A, B and C make greater use of the computer, both to widen the type of mathematics taught and also to enhance the students' learning of mathematics. Mathematics A should be taken in parallel with, or after, Mathematics I; Mathematics B and C should be taken after Mathematics I. Mathematics I, II and III should follow the natural order.

The outline teaching content of the syllabuses is:

Mathematics I: 1. Quadratic functions: quadratic function and its graph, quadratic equations and inequalities. 2. Geometric figures and mensuration; trigonometric ratios, sine and cosine theorems. 3. Treatment of numbers of objects; sequences of natural numbers, permutations and combinations. 4. Probability; basic laws of probability, independent trials, expectation.

Mathematics II: 1. Functions; exponential function, logarithmic function, trigonometric functions and the addition theorems. 2. Geometric figures and equations; coordinates of point, equations of straight line and of circle. 3. Functions and change; differential coefficient and derivatives, applications, idea of integration.

Mathematics III: 1. Functions and limits; rational and irrational functions, composite functions and inverse function, limits of sequences and of functions. 2. Differential calculus; differentiation of sums, products and quotients of functions and of composite functions, applications. 3. Integral calculus; indefinite and definite integrals, integration by substitution, simple integration by parts, applications to eg area, volume, distance.

Mathematics A: 1. Numbers and algebraic expressions; number systems, polynomials, identities and inequalities. 2. Plane geometry; properties of plane figures, basic theorems, loci, geometric transformations in the plane. 3. Number sequences; series and its sum, recurrence relations, mathematical induction, binomial theorem. 4. Computation and the computer; operation of computer, flow charts and programs, computation using a computer.

Mathematics B: 1. Vectors; vectors in the plane, addition of vectors, inner product, vectors in space, coordinates in space. 2. Complex numbers and the complex plane; solutions of equations, Argand diagram, De Moivre's theorem. 3. Probability distributions; calculation of probability, random variables and probability distributions, binomial distribution. 4. Algorithms and the computer; function of computer, programs for various algorithms.

Mathematics C: 1. Matrices and linear computation; matrices and their operations, inverse matrix, system of linear equations, solution by elimination. 2. Curves; equations, ellipse and hyperbola, parametric representation, polar coordinates. 3. Numerical computation; approximate solution of equations (Newton, bisection), numerical integration, approximate computation of area. 4. Statistics; arrangement of data, representative values and measures of dispersion, correlation, populations and samples, normal distribution, idea of statistical inference.

LUXEMBOURG

Age (yr)	Grade			
5-6	K	Pre-school		
6-7	1	Primary School		
7-8	2			
8-9	3			
9-10	4			
10-11	5			
11-12	6			
12-13	7	Lycée (lower cycle)	Lycée Technique	Enseignement complémentaire (Vocational schools)
13-14	8			
14-15	9			
15-16	10	upper cycle	middle cycle	
16-17	11			
17-18	12		upper cycle	
18-19	13			

Notes

1. Pre-school education is optional from age 4, but obligatory from age 5.

2. Children must pass a 12+ examination in French, German and arithmetic in order to enter a lycée. A somewhat easier examination must be passed to gain entrance to a lycée technique. About 20% attend the pre-vocational schools.

LUXEMBOURG

Luxembourg has only 360,000 inhabitants of whom more than 25% are immigrants (Portuguese, Italians, ...). It has 10 lycées or grammar schools (2 of which are private), and 14 (3 private) lycées techniques or technical schools.

Yet the value of a national curriculum is not to be measured in terms of the number of students who follow it. The geographical position of Luxembourg and its linguistic and cultural tensions give it a special interest. Moreover, the way in which the curriculum is organised, in particular, the variety of differentiated mathematics courses in the technical area, should prove of interest to those countries offering a single homogeneous course to their students.

The Luxembourg 'language', which is not a written one, is very near to German. For that reason, German is the first language of instruction in the primary schools and in those pre-vocational schools in which students are not fluent in French. The lycées and lycées techniques, however, teach mathematics in French. Local textbooks are produced for the primary and pre-vocational schools, but other secondary schools use French, Belgian or German textbooks as appropriate.

Unlike most continental countries, compulsory education in Luxembourg begins at age 5. The first year, however, is spent in 'pre-school' education.

Primary School

Primary school teachers teach all subjects. The route into teaching is usually 'lycée' plus three years study in the national teacher-training institute.

The primary school syllabus is extremely detailed (some 100 pages) with many examples and pedagogical hints. We give below only a brief description of the syllabus which is set out grade by grade.

Grade 1 (6–7)

Natural numbers to 20; reading and writing numerals; simple addition and subtraction; multiplication by 2 and 3; units of length (m, cm), weight (kg) and volume (ℓ); recognising and classifying squares, rectangles and triangles.

Grade 2 (7–8)

Natural numbers to 100; addition and subtraction, written algorithms for addition, practical examples; multiplication tables; division by 2.
Measures of length (dm, mm), time and money.
Simple geometrical figures and shapes with practical examples.

Grade 3 (8–9)

Natural numbers to 1000; the four operations; written algorithms for subtraction; practical arithmetic; division without remainders; the fraction a/b as an operator.
The metric system for length, weight, capacity (k, d, c, m), the calendar and the clock.
Drawing lines – parallel and perpendicular.
Straight lines, segments, area.

Grade 4 (9–10)

Natural numbers to one hundred thousand; written algorithms for multiplication and for division by two digit numbers; representation of fractions.
Further units of weight and capacity; measures of time (year, month,..., second); measures of area (m^2, cm^2, mm^2).
Sides and angles of figures; areas of squares and rectangles; symmetry; practical examples.

Grade 5 (10–11)

Natural numbers to one billion; divisors, multiples, primes, decomposition into factors; fractions (representation by areas); decimals and decimal fractions, their addition and subtraction; multiplication and division of fractions.
Revision of units of magnitude.
Lines: parallelism, perpendicularity, intersections.
Area of parallelogram; cube, cuboid; faces, edges and sides; nets of 3–D figures.
Practical examples.

Grade 6 (11–12)

Revision of the four operations on the naturals; equivalence of fractions; conversion of decimals to vulgar fractions and vice–versa; multiplication and division of decimals.
Elementary statistics: arithmetic mean, frequencies.

Practical examples
Circles and angles; right angles; perimeters of square and rectangle; area of parallelogram and triangle; volume and surface area of cube and cuboid; practical examples.
Percentages; rule of three; examples on division (fractions); examples from day–to–day life.

Vocational Schools

As in some other countries, students who enter the vocational schools are those who have gained very little mathematical knowledge and understanding at primary school. In Luxembourg they concentrate, therefore, on the re–teaching of primary school mathematics. Transfers are possible from the pre–vocational to the technical schools.

Technical Schools

The technical schools, like the lycées, have teachers who have usually studied for a degree in France, Belgium, Germany, or Switzerland, and have later satisfactorily completed a three–year probationary period including pedagogical training, the presentation of a scientific dissertation, and a final examination (including demonstration lessons and the correction and marking of written work). However, the technical schools also have, for example, certificated engineers and architects on their staff.

The first three grades of the technical school are referred to as the 'cycle of orientation and observation'. Mathematics is compulsory in these years. There then follows the two–year 'cycle moyen technique'. This contains a number of subdivisions containing mathematics, but also a vocational stream (3 years) which does not. Finally, in the 'cycle supérieur', there are two streams, 'administrative' and 'technical', both of which include mathematics and provide access to university study, and a two–year course aimed at the training of technicians which also includes mathematics.

Cycle d'observation et d'orientation

Grade 7 (12–13) 5 hours per week

Elementary set theory, subsets, union, intersection.

Plane geometry including standard figures.
Elementary coordinate geometry.
Negative numbers (integers), addition and subtraction.
Basic solids (cube, cylinder, sphere, etc.).

Grade 8 (13–14) 4 hours per week

Revision of sets; relations, mappings, bijections.
Proportion, percentage, interest.
Plane geometry; angles, triangles.
Natural numbers; powers, multiples, divisors, Euclidean algorithm, primes, prime factorisation, lcm, hcf.
Integers, multiplication, powers.
Reals, the four operations.
Introduction to algebra; equations, transformation of formulae.

Grade 9 (14–15)

Three levels of mathematics are offered. Level 1 (4 hours a week) has a large algebra component (polynomials, factorisation, algebraic fractions, equations), and also the geometry of triangles and rectangles (eg constructions and congruent triangles). Level 2 (3 hours) has less algebra, and lays more emphasis on ratio, percentage, and powers of 10 and their connection with the metric system. Level 3 (3 hours) introduces some statistics, 'commercial' arithmetic and mensuration, simple geometrical constructions and scale-drawing, but does not introduce formal algebra (other than formulae for mensuration, etc.). Level 3 students will continue in the vocational stream.

Cycle moyen (Grades 10–11, 15–17)

Again the numerous alternatives mean that only brief indications of content can be given.

The 'artisanal et industriel' stream devotes 3 hours a week to mathematics. The syllabus for grade 10 includes vectors, Pythagoras, Thales, and trigonometry (up to scalar product of vectors and its trigonometrical significance); inequations, simultaneous linear equations in up to 3 variables, powers and roots, logarithms and quadratic equations. In the eleventh grade there is revision and further work on cartesian geometry (lines, circles, vector and cartesian equations, etc.), a study of basic functions (linear and quadratic, square root, modulus, reciprocal, etc.), trigonometry (equations, sine and cosine rules), and further geometrical properties (tangents, chords of circles, similar triangles, formulae for lengths of sides of triangles, etc).

The 'administratif et commercial' stream follows a somewhat different course (still, 3 hours per week for both years). In Grade 10 the emphasis is on algebraic revision, functions, inequalities, powers and roots, logarithms, quadratics, right-angled triangles (Pythagoras) and statistics (mean, mode, median, variance). Grade 11 contains analytical geometry, trigonometry, 3-D geometry, algebra (quadratics, APs, GPs).

Cycle supérieur (17-19)

Again, the course is divided into several streams.

Students in the 'administrative' division can take two mathematics courses. The 'section gestion' (2½ hours per week in Grade 12, 3 hours per week in Grade 13) offers in the first year, analysis (limits, continuity, differentiation (polynomials)), study of functions, combinatorics and probability, and statistics. In Grade 13 the students study the exponential and logarithmic functions, integration (via primitives, by substitution and by parts, applications to areas and surfaces), statistics (various representations, measures of position and spread, bivariate distributions, correlation and regression) and probability (binomial, normal distributions). The 'secrétariat' section (2 hours in Grade 12 only) is less demanding: some simple statistics and much commercial arithmetic (percentages, margins, interest (simple and compound), annuities, etc). (The set texts are 'Mathématiques appliquées à l'économie', and 'Mathématiques financières'.)

Students in the 'technique général' stream spend considerable time studying mathematics: 5 hours per week in Grade 12 and 7 hours in Grade 13. The Grade 12 algebra syllabus comprises, matrices and determinants (simultaneous equations, Cramer's rule, systems with parameters), quadratics (including properties of roots, and systems of equations of either one linear and one quadratic, or two quadratics (including geometrical interpretation)) and complex numbers. Trigonometry includes the general circular functions, radian measure, and relations in a triangle. The notion of a linear space is introduced along with scalar and vector products and the line, circle and conics are studied in analytical geometry. Analysis begins with the study of sequences, series, limits (including operations on limits) and continuity before differentiation is introduced. This is taken as far as the usual rules, Rolle's Theorem, and approximations in the case of small increments. Grade 13 is devoted entirely to the differential and integral calculus: primitives, logarithmic and exponential functions, the trigonometric functions and their inverses, Taylor, Maclaurin, the

Binomial theorem, integration by parts and substitution, partial fractions, areas and volumes, first order differential equations (variables separable, homogeneous, linear).

The third section of the 'cycle supérior' is that for the 'formation de technicien'. The 12th grade (3½ hours) course for the 'mechanics' includes equations (logarithmic and exponential), roots, trigonometry, matrices (including simultaneous linear equations), complex numbers, series and sequences, functions, differentiation of polynomials, the chain rule. Grade 13 (Applied mathematics - 2 hours per week) revises and extends differentiation (transcendental functions, curve sketching) and introduces integration. Simple applications are made to areas, volumes, curve length, and statics (moments, centre of gravity). Other disciplines follow a roughly similar course.

Lycée secondaire

The lycée secondaire is organised in two cycles or key stages.

The lower cycle comprises Grades 7–9 and, in this, mathematics is compulsory. The higher cycle, Grades 10–13, may offer four to six streams: A languages, B maths and physics, C chemistry and biology, D economics, E arts (fine), F arts (music). The number of hours allotted to mathematics varies from stream to stream and in Grade 13 of stream A no mathematics is taught.

The Abitur or Examen de fin d'études secondaires, is taken at the end of Grade 13 and gives access to all universities. The examination is identical for corresponding streams in all lycées and consists solely of written tests.

The syllabus is presented in a very closed form. There is a set text (Belgian or French) and the syllabus prescribes the chapters (and sections of these) to be studied. The number of formal written class tests to be given in each of the three terms of a year is also stipulated.

Since the syllabus is largely a derived one, for the texts must be imported, we shall not describe it in full.

The syllabus for the lower cycle still places emphasis on sets, relations, functions, mappings and transformation geometry (this is true also of that for Grade 8 which was revised for the 1989–90 session). Probability and statistics are not taught in these years and little emphasis is laid on practical matters.

Two textbooks are used in Grade 10, one for sections B and C, the other for sections A, D, E and F. The respective time allocations per week for mathematics are A 3 lessons, B 5, C 4, D 3, E 3, F 3.

Section B covers algebraic operations, square roots, Thales, addition and scalar multiplication of vectors, cartesian coordinates (lines), linear equations and inequalities in two unknowns, metric relations in a triangle, normal and orthogonal vectors, angles, circles, the first elements of trigonometry and 3–D geometry. Section C offers a slightly slimmed down version of this; 3–D geometry and a more intuitive approach to vectors. Section D covers square roots, Thales, vectors, lines, equations and inequalities, the right–angled triangle, angles, an introduction to geometry. Sections A, E and F treat roughly the same material but often more succinctly.

This same pattern continues in the 11th grade. Now Section B introduces logic (De Morgan etc.), permutations and combinations, probability and the binomial theorem. Algebraic techniques and coordinate and vector geometry are developed and the concept of a metric space introduced together with work on, for example, logarithms and calculators. The non–specialist, A, D, E, F streams take a less abstract approach and cover such topics as operations on sets, lines, systems of equations and inequalities, the general quadratic, parabolas, graphical representation of functions, trigonometric functions, the scalar product and elementary statistics and probability. (Note; there are differences between the streams, eg A and D do not study probability.)

In the final two grades the number of periods allocated for mathematics changes

	A	B	C	D	E	F
Grade 12	3	6	4	3	3	3
Grade 13	–	8	5	4	3	2

The mathematics specialists (B) pay particular attention in Grade 12 to linear spaces, transformations and vectors; sequences, limits, continuity, and differentiation. Section F students meet APs and GPs, differentiation and integration (primitives), statistics and vectors in the plane.

In the final grade, the B stream looks in more detail at algebraic structures and geometrical transformations (4 periods per week – to include also conics and complex numbers) and analysis (logarithmic and exponential functions, integration with applications, and differential equations).

Section F (now reduced to 2 periods a week) concentrates on integration (primitives) and the logarithmic and exponential functions.

It is of interest that the final examinations for sections D, E and F do not contain questions of a theoretical nature.

It will be appreciated, then, that although a very small country, Luxembourg still offers its students a very wide range of mathematics courses.

THE NETHERLANDS

<table>
<tr><th>Age (yr)</th><th>Grade</th><th colspan="4"></th></tr>
<tr><td>5-6</td><td>K</td><td colspan="4" rowspan="7">Basic Education</td></tr>
<tr><td>6-7</td><td>1</td></tr>
<tr><td>7-8</td><td>2</td></tr>
<tr><td>8-9</td><td>3</td></tr>
<tr><td>9-10</td><td>4</td></tr>
<tr><td>10-11</td><td>5</td></tr>
<tr><td>11-12</td><td>6</td></tr>
<tr><td>12-13</td><td>7</td><td rowspan="6">Pre-university (VWO) 20%</td><td rowspan="5">Higher general (HAVO) 24%</td><td rowspan="4">Inter-mediate general (MAVO) 34%</td><td rowspan="4">Lower Vocat-ional (LBO) 21%</td></tr>
<tr><td>13-14</td><td>8</td></tr>
<tr><td>14-15</td><td>9</td></tr>
<tr><td>15-16</td><td>10</td></tr>
<tr><td>16-17</td><td>11</td><td colspan="2"></td></tr>
<tr><td>17-18</td><td>12</td><td colspan="3"></td></tr>
</table>

Notes

1. Nursery and primary education are now combined in one school–type, "basic education". Children may start at the age of 4, compulsory education begins at the age of 5. Basic education is taught by "class teachers", later grades by subject specialists.

2. Transfer between different streams is possible, but usually at the cost of "backtracking" one year, eg from the end of MAVO to Grade 10 of HAVO and from the end of HAVO to Grade 11 of VWO. In Grade 7, the various streams share the same curriculum. This facilitates the immediate transfer of students who may have been incorrectly streamed.

3. A governmental working group is currently devising new programmes for mathematics for all school types in the age range 12–16 (Grades 7–10).

THE NETHERLANDS

The educational system of the Netherlands is particularly noteworthy for the way in which secondary education is divided into four well–defined streams (possibly with two or more available within the same school), each catering for between 20 and 35 per cent of the student age cohort. Students themselves opt for a particular stream on the advice of the head of the primary school.

Schools are also partitioned by secular/religious considerations. However, the mathematics curricula followed are not significantly affected by this form of division.

Basic (primary) education has a school year of about 40 weeks and throughout its duration about 5 hours a week are given over to teaching mathematics.

The mathematics is defined by means of a school working plan, set by the school board after approval by an inspector. The ministry is currently working on a list of final objectives to be adopted nationally.

The syllabus for basic education is not broken down into years but is presented as overall aims and objectives up to Grade 6.

The general aims are to attain basic skills and understanding in arithmetic, measurement and geometry, to develop good attitudes to work in general, to see how mathematics is applied and how the subject is connected with 'real life', to become used to the language of mathematics and, through investigations and other activities, to comprehend the connections between rules, patterns and structures.
Counting, tables, mental arithmetic, estimations and the ability to apply the four operations are seen as basic. Other curriculum contents include: place value and notation, ratio and percentage, fractions and decimal fractions, measurement (including metric units for length, weight, volume), and geometry.

The list of basic skills includes: counting forwards and backwards, addition, subtraction, multiplication and division tables by heart, mental arithmetic, estimation, working with 'rough' approximations, use of calculator, the four operations and the positional system, comparison of ratios, ratios of quantities (weight–price, distance–time etc.), global estimation, percentage, everyday applications, percentage as a growth factor, relations with fractions and decimal fractions, comparison of fractions, the four operations with fractions (based on concrete situations), tables of ratios, the number line, appreciating correctness of operations, decimals, estimation with decimals, time, money, length, weight, temperature, probability (likely – unlikely), area, volume, speed, the metric system, estimation of measurements, tables, graphs, time–tables, weather charts, simple statistical tests, the mean, shadow images of geometrical shapes, triangle, square, cuboid, cube, sphere, 3–D plans and maps, simple coordinate systems, constructing a 3–D body from relevant 2–D images, reflection, rotation, symmetry, simple properties of 3–D solids and 2–D shapes.

At secondary level the syllabus is defined very concisely and not necessarily by specific grade. In some cases, content to be covered within a 'key stage' is given, in others the syllabus is essentially described (as used to be the case in England) through that for the examination taken in the final year of the school–type. The mathematics curriculum for the first (or 'bridge') year of secondary education (Grade 7) is more or less common to all school types and mathematics is taught for four 50–minute periods a week. (Secondary school years have about 38 weeks.) The syllabuses for Grades 7–10 are currently under review. A report will appear in August 1992 and there are likely to be radical changes.

Apart from the final examination all assessment is internal (books of tests and exercises are published nationally). It is not unusual for students to have to repeat years.

Grade 7 (12–13)

Sets
The sets of natural numbers, integers, rational numbers, number line (rationals), ordering.
The four operations, powers with positive integer exponents.
Simple first degree equations and inequalities in one variable.
Commutative, associative and distributive properties, use of brackets in simple expressions, factorisation.
Introduction to geometry: cube, cuboid, plane, line, point, angle, distances, triangle, quadrangle, circle.
Transformations: line symmetry, point symmetry, translations, rotations.
Parallelism of lines.
Congruence of figures.
Properties of triangles and quadrilaterals: kite, parallelogram, rhombus, rectangle, square.
Point sets and their intersection.

MAVO and LBO school–types

The MAVO and LBO streams share the same mathematics curriculum. However, for both mathematics is only compulsory until Grade 8. Pupils need not take the final, school–leaving examination in mathematics. About 70% of MAVO students take this examination as against roughly 55% of LBO students. Those who take the examination may do so at two levels: the lower level, C, and the higher level, D (MAVO students must take at least three subjects at level D). Students must take the leaving examination in six subjects. LBO students are also offered the opportunity to sit school examinations at two lower levels than C.

Three hours per week are devoted on average to mathematics in Grade 8, and (for those continuing to study the subject) 3 hours per week in Grade 9, and 4 hours per week in Grade 10.

Grade 8 (13–14, compulsory)

Irrational numbers.
Measurement: lengths, areas and volume: Pythagoras' Theorem.
First degree equations and inequalities in one variable.
Relations: graphs of a simple relation, two linear equations in two variables.
Point sets in the plane (e.g. mediators, bisectors, etc. and their construction).
Functions: graph of a function, linear and simple quadratics, solution of simple quadratic equations.
Introduction to descriptive statistics.

Grades 9 and 10 (LBO and MAVO examination classes) (14–16)

Linear inequalities in two unknowns.
Quadratics: equations and inequalities.
Vectors in the plane: operations, similar figures.
The trigonometric functions, sine, cosine and tangent; sine and cosine rules.
Calculation of angles and distances in the plane and in space.
In the plane: equations of line and circle, points of intersection and tangents; angles and distance.
Further descriptive statistics.

Examination syllabuses (LBO–MAVO)

	Programme C		Programme D
1.	Simple descriptive statistics	1.	Descriptive statistics
2.	Relations: graph of a linear relation.	2.	Relations: As C, but more general. In the plane, equations of line and circle; points of intersection and tangents, angles and distance.
3.	Functions: graph of a function, linear and simple quadratic functions	3.	As C, but more general quadratic functions
4.	Linear equations and in–equalities with one unknown	4.	As C
5.	Two linear equations in two unknowns	5.	As C, plus linear inequalities in two unknowns
6.	Simple quadratic equations	6.	Quadratic equations and inequalities
7.	Line and point symmetry translations, rotations composition of trans–formations, congruence and similarity of figures	7.	As C, plus vectors in the plane
8.	Measurement: length, area and volume; Pythagoras; point sets in the plane	8.	As C
9.	Simple calculation of angles and distances in the plane and in space	9.	As C, but more complicated examples
10.	Sine, cosine, tangent	10.	As C, plus sine and cosine rules

[There follow a number of brief observations on the contents of the syllabus and on the examination, eg that angle measure is to be in degrees, the convention for lettering sides of the triangle ABC, and that frequency, frequency table, histogram, mode, mean and median are expected to be understood under descriptive statistics.]

HAVO

Within the HAVO school–type, mathematics is compulsory until the end of grade 9. On average, mathematics occupies 3 periods a week in grades 8 and 9, and 4 per week in later grades. (The hours prescribed for mathematics relate to a minimal total over the 'key stage'.) During grades 10 and 11 students must select 6 subjects in which they wish to take the final examination. In 1989 only 63% of HAVO students opted to take the final examination in mathematics.

In an attempt to increase that percentage, an alternative mathematics syllabus (already trialled in twenty five schools) will be offered from 1992. The two syllabuses, A and B, will have different biases. Mathematics A is particularly suitable for those wishing to go on to higher education and study subjects in which mathematics does not play a major role (eg social studies, economics, primary school teaching). Mathematics B is meant to meet the needs of future non–university technicians, engineers, mathematicians and physical scientists.

Again, the syllabuses given are very concise indeed, thus permitting some gradual changes in emphasis and content **without** the need for official revision of the programme. In essence, the details are determined by the leaving examinations, text books (of which teachers have a free choice) and the teachers. Syllabuses are given for two–year 'stages', rather than by grade.

Grades 8 and 9 (13–15)

Irrational numbers
Measure: length, area, volume; properties of right–angled triangles
First degree equations and inequalities in one variable
Relations: graphs of a first degree relation; two linear equations in two unknowns; linear inequalities with two variables
Point sets in the plane
Functions: graphs; linear and quadratic functions, equations and inequalities
Vectors in the plane: operations; similarity of figures
Introduction to descriptive statistics
Sine, cosine, tangent; sine and cosine rules
Simple calculations of angles and distances in the plane and in space

Grades 10 and 11 (15–17)

The syllabuses for these two grades will be changed after 1991.

Below we give the syllabuses for the final examinations for the two new courses, Mathematics A and B. Again the syllabuses are accompanied by short notes giving some further details.

Examination Syllabus HAVO A

Tables, graphs and formulae

Tables, graphs as a representation of the connection between two variables, changes, maxima and minima, the concept of differences and the quotient of differences, the Δ notation, periodicity, trends, graphs, related functions; representation of a three-dimensional form by a series of two-dimensional graphs, formulae as a means of representation of the connections between two or more variables, linear functions, $y = ax + b$, linear interpolation and extrapolation, solution of linear simultaneous equations, rational and power functions, $y = a/x + b$, $y = ax^b$ (rational b), exponential functions, $y = ab^x$, asymptotic behaviour, composition of functions, substituting a formula in a formula.

Discrete mathematics

'Distances' in various contexts (geographical, social), tabular (matrix) representation, graphs, vertices, edges, directed graphs, matrix representations (adjacency, etc.), isomorphism of graphs, networks, matrices and models of dynamic processes, operations on matrices, addition and multiplication, identity matrix, use of matrices in applications, combinatorics, tree diagrams, shortest paths, Pascal's triangle, combinations of k from n, applications, binary codes.

Statistics and probability

Populations and samples, statistical data and their graphical representation, characteristics of a frequency distribution, mean, mode, median, spread, standard deviation, quartiles, the normal distribution, Galton board, standard normal distribution and table, applications, probability and expectation, calculations with probabilities, the binomial distribution.

Examination syllabus HAVO B

Applied Analysis

Standard functions, x^r , sin x , cos x , tan x , a^x , $\log_a x$, graphs, equations, solutions using calculator, operations with functions, y = f(x) and related graphs (f(x) + c , f(x+c) etc), equations and inequalities, linear and quadratic equations, algebraic and graphical solutions of simultaneous equations, solutions of inequalities, gradients, measures of change, quotient of differences, differential coefficient, derived functions, notation, second derivatives, applications, rules of differentiation (product, quotient, chain), tangents, points of inflexion, extreme values, asymptotic behaviour, periodic functions, radians, amplitude, frequency, y = a sin(bx+c) + d , symmetry properties of trigonometric functions, solution of simple trigonometrical equations, simple identities, exponential functions, properties of exponents ($a^u a^v$ etc.), exponential function as a model of growth, half-life and other growth factors, logarithmic functions, inverse of exponential, different bases, properties, solution of equations, transform of $y = ca^x$ etc.

Geometry in 3-D

[Plane geometry and trigonometry, mensuration of common figures, n-gons, Pythagoras and cosine rule] Properties of common solids, points, lines and planes, incidence relations, transformations and reflections in space, projections (central, parallel), descriptive geometry, constructions, images from different viewpoints, distances (point-point, point-line, etc.), angles (line-line, line-plane, etc.), surface areas and volumes.

Pre-university education (VWO)

Reform of the VWO curricula preceded those of the HAVO. The two reforms, however, have shared features. In 1985 a new mathematics syllabus, Mathematics A, was introduced intended for those 11th and 12th grade students who did not see mathematics forming a substantial part of their future studies. In 1989, 59% of all VWO students opted to take this as one of their seven final examination subjects. (Note that VWO students take one more subject than HAVO students.) The course for would-be mathematicians, scientists and engineers was taken by 46% of students. The courses differ in aim and content and it is permissible to offer both as examinable subjects: 18% of students opted to do this, thus leaving 13% of students opting not to take a final examination in mathematics.

The syllabus for the VWO students is, in fact, even leaner than that for the HAVO school. A programme is given for the compulsory grades 8, 9 and 10, and the two examination syllabuses are prescribed. The national society of mathematics teachers is currently working on a more detailed interpretation of the final examination syllabus for Mathematics A.

Grades 8–10 (13–16)

Sets in conjunction with elementary logic operations
First degree equations and inequalities in one or two unknowns
The set of real numbers
Square roots: second degree equations and inequalities
Point sets
Composition of two reflections and two translations

Vectors: calculations with vectors: links between components and point co-ordinates
Similarity transformations, similarity of figures
Centroid of a triangle; area; theorem of Pythagoras
Trigonometrical ratios; sine, cosine, tangent; sine and cosine rules
3–D figures; contour lines; co-ordinates in space; distance and angles in 3–D; volume
Functions and graphs; linear and quadratic functions; absolute value; roots; simple trigonometric functions
Inverse functions; composition of functions; the exponential and logarithmic functions
Introduction to the differential calculus
Introduction to descriptive statistics; elementary probability.

Final Examination (VWO) Mathematics A

Applied Analysis

Graphs of functions: drawing conclusions from graphs,
Derived function as a measure of change, tangents to a graph
Rules for differentiation
Derivatives of rational functions and roots
Optimisation
Periodic functions: trigonometric functions and in particular $y = a \sin b(x+c) + d$ as a model of periodic changes

Trends
Differentiation of trigonometric functions
Growth: $y = ba^x$ as a model for exponential growth
The number e ; logarithmic function
Use of logarithmic and log–log graph paper
Differentiation of exponential functions

Applied Algebra

Matrices, in particular, data–, incidence– and transition matrices
Operations with matrices (scalar multiplication, addition, subtraction and multiplication) and models in which these are employed.
Functions of several variables: linear programming; graphical methods for problems with two or three variables; contour lines and planes.

Probability and Statistics

Critical inspection of statistical data
Frequency tables, histograms, cumulative frequency, mean, mode, median
Populations, samples
Conditional probability and independence
Probability distributions, in particular, binomial and hypergeometric distributions
Expected value and standard deviation
Normal distribution and use of the standard table
Hypothesis testing, confidence intervals

Informatics

Algorithms with applications to the micro
Structural schemas
Simple programs and programming
Use of standard programs and interpretation of output

Options

For a limited period of three years one of the following options is added to the programme:
partial differentiation of functions of two variables

the simplex method for linear programming
difference equations
matrix algebra
statistics (correlation, regression, use of software)

Final Examination (VWO) Mathematics B

Analysis

Polynomial functions
Rational functions and roots
Logarithmic and exponential functions, e
The trigonometric functions – including inverse functions
Even and odd functions
Graphs of these functions
Solutions of simultaneous equations and inequalities
Trigonometric formulae: $\sin(x \pm y)$, $\sin 2x$, $\sin x \pm \sin y$, etc
Limits, continuity and discontinuity of functions
Differentiability, derived functions, rules for differentiation
Drawing graphs, tangents, cusp, point of inflexion, asymptote
Monotonicity, extreme points
Primitive functions (integration), definite integral
Areas and volumes
Differential equations, direction fields, solution curves, solution of elementary differential equations
Parametric representation

Geometry

Points, lines and planes
Intersection of planes with prisms and pyramids
Vector representation and equations of lines and planes; perpendiculars and orthogonal projection
Reflections, translations and rotations in space
Scalar (inner) product, normal vector to a plane, angles and distances
Sphere, cylinder and cone with tangent lines and planes
Solids of revolution and calculation of volumes.

PORTUGAL

Age (yr)	Grade	Present	Proposed
5-6	K	Pre-school	Pre-school
6-7	1	Primary	First cycle
7-8	2		
8-9	3		
9-10	4		
10-11	5	Middle	Second cycle
11-12	6		
12-13	7	Lower Secondary	Third cycle
13-14	8		
14-15	9		
15-16	10	Upper Secondary	Secondary
16-17	11		
17-18	12		

Notes

1. Pre–school exists but is not compulsory. It is intended to develop this part of the system.

2. At present, "Secondary education" divides into five areas in Grade 10. In future, there will be two streams from 15+, 'academic' and 'professional'. The former stream will be divided into the four areas: science, technology and engineering, letters and literature, and arts.

PORTUGAL

The school system of Portugal is in many ways the least developed of those of the EC countries. Currently, great attempts are being made to extend the provision of education by raising the school–leaving age from 12 (six years of compulsory education) to 15. Thus, as in Spain which is currently moving its school–leaving age from 14 to 16, new syllabuses are being developed which have to apply to a totally new school population. This change has led to considerable debate within the educational community. Official national programmes for all school levels exist, and now suggestions for changes are being made by teacher associations, teacher training institutions, etc.

In the first four grades (formerly 'primary' now '1st cycle') mathematics is subsumed under general education, ie no specific time–tabled hours are allotted for mathematics teaching. However, there is a mathematics curriculum set out which should be covered. Mathematics is a separate time–tabled entity from grade 5 on. In the 35–week school year, four hours/periods a week are devoted to the subject in grades 5–9 (2nd and 3rd cycles). In grades 10 and 11, students opt for one of five areas – four of these include mathematics and the subject is allotted five hours per week. Grade 12 is currently a specialised 'pre–university' grade. In future it will become more like grades 10 and 11 and the present examination at the end of grade 11 will be abolished. In future, mathematics will be taught for four hours a week in all grades.

Portugal still makes considerable use of 'retention' of students – promotion is not automatic (except usually at the end of grades 1 and 3). Assessment is internal and is based on written tests plus work through the year. At the "upper secondary" level there are national examinations. Mathematics is a subject particularly associated with failure and repetition and the area 'Letters and Literature' which has no mathematical component proves a very popular option – probably because of the perceived difficulty of mathematics.

No special provision for differing mathematical ability is made (other than repetition of years). Bearing this fact in mind, the Portuguese syllabuses appear very demanding in comparison with, say, the English national curriculum.

Primary school (ages 6–10, grades 1–4)

The national curriculum is presented year by year in terms of various themes. Associated with each theme is a list of specific objectives and accompanying suggested activities. The whole is preceded by an introduction setting out the goals of primary school mathematics and giving hints on methodology (eg the possible use of small group and individualised work). We list below themes and (abbreviated) objectives - occasionally giving suggested activities to exemplify these.

First grade (6–7)

Sets sets, elements, and defining properties; subsets; union of two disjoint sets (leading to addition), complements.

Space and the Foundations of Geometry lines (open and closed curves), interior, exterior, boundary (through physical activities and activities with objects), right, left, above, below, front, behind, before and after; sets with similar geometrical figures; translations using square–grid paper.

Number and numeration correspondences between sets, more than/less than, numbers up to 20 (ordering, decomposition, addition, subtraction, applications) [suggested activity: completing number sequences] identification of ten as the base of numeration system.

Lengths identification and construction of objects of the same length and of different lengths, smaller/greater, notion of units

Surfaces identification and construction of figures with the same and with different measures, notion of units and of a covering.

Volume/capacity equal and different capacities, measure of capacity (units).

Time and order ordinal numbers (first, second), days of the week, the hour as a unit of time.

Weight equal and different weights (heavier/lighter using a balance), units of weight (not necessarily standard).

Second Grade (7–8)

Space and Geometry line segments, symmetry of quadrilaterals using squared paper, polygons, angles.

Numbers and numeration representation of numbers up to 1,000, dozens and 'twenty–fives' (a traditional Portuguese amount) (by partitioning sets of objects), multiplication, commutativity of addition and multiplication, representation of numbers up to 20 in Roman numerals [use of $>$ and $<$ (numbers up to 100) is a suggested activity as are, eg decomposition of numbers in various forms, algorithms for subtraction (two digits with 'carrying') and long multiplication by a single digit number].

Lengths measuring, comparing and constructing line segments of a given length.

Surfaces calculating the number of square units in a rectangle with sides a multiple of the unit, use of multiplication [here and elsewhere activities are suggested which are 'above the minimum level' ie some allowance is made for differentiation by attainment and ability].

Time and order the calendar, months of the year and their varying lengths, hours in a day.

Money notes and coins, buying and selling, decomposition with notes and coins.

Third year (8–9)

Sets subsets, disjoint subsets, partitions into sets with the same number of elements.

Space and geometry right, acute and obtuse angles (without technical names for acute and obtuse), constructing figures symmetric about a given line, use of ruler, set square and compass.

Numbers and numeration tens of thousands as a unit, mental arithmetic (division), relation of division and multiplication, multiplication using different algorithms, division, Roman numerals, decimals; the number line divided into tenths ie displaying numbers of the form 3.4, activities involving measuring and weighing]; relationship between multiplication and division; $^1/_{10}$, $^1/_{100}$, $^1/_{1000}$,..., as possible units.

Lengths the metric system and its units [milli–, centi–, deci–metre, deca–, hecto, kilo, tenths, hundredths, thousandths; relationship with decimals]

Area decomposition and composition, figures with the same area and different shapes.

Volume and capacity identifying bodies with the same volume [decomposition and composition].

Time and order minutes, hours and minutes, reading a clock.

Weights units of weight and their relation [links with decimals], kilo, hecto, deca, gramme, deci, centi, milli.

Money written representation of amounts, national units.

Fourth year (9–10)

Space and geometry 3-D solids; faces, vertices, edges (and their relationships ie two faces meet in an edge); cubes, prisms, pyramids, cylinders, cones, spheres; construction of cubes, etc; nets; use of plumb line and spirit level.

Numbers and numeration numbers up to a million; sums, differences, multiplication of decimals, simple examples of division, [rules for calculating products of 0.1, 0.01 etc, long division].

Area units of area and their relations, applications [decomposition of a square metre into square decimetres, etc, volume and capacity in different units].

Middle Schools (Grades 5–6: currently the last years of compulsory education)

The syllabus for the middle schools is presented in a different form from that for the primary schools. Now the syllabus is essentially divided into two main areas: sets and numbers, and geometry and mensuration. Some basic ideas on algebra are included in the former area. The geometry syllabus bears the imprint of the 1960s emphasis on sets. The syllabus is now much leaner – a list of topics followed by a few observations which usually provide further guidance on matters of content. In these grades children are taught by teachers with specific mathematical qualifications.

Grade 5 (10–11)

Sets and numbers

(a) intuitive notions of sets and elements, representations of sets, defining properties; singletons and empty sets,

(b) membership, identical and different sets, inclusion, subsets,

(c) intuitive notions of correspondence, classes of sets having the same number of elements (idea that there is an integer corresponding to each class), distinction between sets and numbers, singletons correspond to 1, the empty set to 0,

(d) order on numbers, $<$ and $>$,

(e) distinction between numbers and numerals, revision of decimal system, its evolution from the Roman system, use of bar graphs to represent integers,

(f) sets of numbers and their cardinals, natural numbers with zero, finite and infinite sets (intuitive notion).

Operations on sets and integers

(a) intersection and union,

(b) addition of numbers (as cardinal of union of disjoint sets), tables, commutativity, zero as neutral element, repeated addition, associativity, applications to mental arithmetic,

(c) intuitive notions of a complement,

(d) subtraction of numbers (use of complementary set), subtraction as inverse of addition, solution of equations of the form $a + x = b$, $a - x = b$, $x - a = b$,

(e) use of brackets (simple examples) 'of' and 'x' ,

(f) multiplications of numbers, 1 as neutral (identity) element, 0 as an 'absorbing' element, distributivity, successive multiplications, associativity,

(g) writing and calculating numerical expressions,

(h) powers of a number – addition, subtraction and multiplication of powers,

(i) division, as inverse of multiplication, special cases of divisor and dividend, division of a product by a factor, solution of $ax = b$, $x \div a = b$, $a \div x = b$, remainders, intuitive criteria for divisibility by 2, 5, 10, 100,

(j) writing and calculating simple numerical examples.

Rational numbers

a half of, a third of, a half, a third, two thirds of, two thirds, correspondence between the preposition 'of' and the fraction as an operator, applications to sharing/partitioning examples, equivalent fractions, transformation of fractions with denominators 2, 5, 50, 20, 25 and 4 to decimal equivalents, decimals to vulgar fractions, fractions representing numbers less than, equal to, or greater than 1, mixed fractions, the set of rationals.

Elements of geometry

(a) bodies as subsets of space; solids, cubes, parallelepipeds, prisms etc; solids in technology, art and nature – pictures, crystals, stones, glass polyhedral ornaments,

(b) surface (or boundary) of a solid – interior and exterior, open and closed surfaces, boundary of an open surface,

(c) lines in space, open and closed curves, straight lines in space, extremes of a line segment – points,

(d) planes, defining properties of a plane, the plane as an unbounded surface, half–planes,

(e) order of points on a line (comparison with time, 'before' and 'after'), half–line, use of 'between' applied to points on a line, a line segment as the set of points between its extremal points,

(f) closed curves in a plane, interior, exterior, sets of points, boundary, domains, convex and non–convex domains, polygons, circumference as the boundary of a circle, chords, segments,

(g) the class of line segments of equal length,

(h) perimeters of polygons and circles,

(i) revision of measures of length,

(j) radius, chords, diameter, circumference of a circle, π (as a non–recurring decimal, approximate value, applications), $c = \pi d$,

(k) half–lines with a common origin, convex and non–convex angles, classes of angles of the same size (measure),

(l) sums of angles – right, acute, obtuse angles, bisector of an angle,

(m) measure of angles, units, degrees, minutes and seconds, use of a protractor,

(n) angle properties of the circle, distinction between the angle subtended by an arc and its length,

(o) internal angle of a polygon, etymology of triangle, quadrilateral, pentagon, etc, regular polygons, classification of triangles by sides and angles.

Grade 6 (11–12)

Sets and Integers

(a) revision of divisors, sets of divisors, highest common factors, mutually prime numbers,

(b) revision of multiples, sets of multiples, least common multiple.

Rational numbers

(a) revision of the concepts of fractions, equivalent fractions, rationals, application to the simplification of fractions, comparison of magnitude of fractions with different denominators,

(b) addition and subtraction of rationals; simple cases of vulgar fractions, addition and subtraction of rationals in decimal form, use of letters in formulae which exemplify the properties of addition,

(c) numerical examples involving addition, subtraction and at most the use of a single pair of brackets (mixed fractions and decimals),

(d) multiplication of rationals (vulgar fractions and decimals), distributivity, use of letters,

(e) numerical examples involving addition, subtraction, multiplication and brackets, use of decimals and mixed fractions,

(f) notion of powers for integers and fractions, properties of powers,

(g) division of rationals, $ax = b$ $(a \neq 0)$ where a and b are integers, rules for dividing two rationals, dividing decimals,

(h) simple numerical examples including the four operations,

(i) problems leading to, and solutions of, equations of the form $ax = b$, $x + a = b$, $a + x = b$,

(j) numerical equalities of the type $a/b = c/d$, introduction to the expressions ratio, proportion, least and greatest, verification that $a/b = c/d$ is equivalent to $ad = bc$, solution of equations on proportion.

Magnitudes and proportionality

(a) correspondences between the set of values of one magnitude and that of another, notion of direct proportionality [significance of the constant of proportionality],

(b) problems of mixing substances,

(c) notion of percentage, equivalence of such expressions as $38\% = 38/100 = .38$, calculation of percentages (direct and making use of real life situations), interpretation of pie charts and bar and column graphs,

(d) calculation of interest (simple in years and fractions of years) and tax.

Elements of 2– and 3–D geometry

(a) lines in the plane, concurrency and parallelism, notions of direction, perpendicularity, distance of a point from a line, parallel lines in space, drawing parallel lines with ruler and set square, distance between parallel lines, trapeziums and parallelograms, classification of parallelograms,

(b) vertical lines, applications to building, plumbline, horizontal planes, spirit level, horizontal lines,

(c) intersection of a line with a circle (in the plane), different cases, intersection of two circles, radius and tangent property, common tangent to two circles.

Surfaces and area

(a) problems of land measurement, historical examples, etymology of 'geometry', passage from concrete examples to abstract ones, decomposition into neighbouring surfaces, equal surfaces, notion of area, equal area does not imply geometrical congruence,

(b) revision of area of rectangle and square, metric units (and local agricultural units), formulae for areas of rectangle and square, link with 'square of a number',

(c) formulae for area of parallelograms, triangles, polygons (by decomposition into triangles or into triangles and parallelograms), regular polygons,

(d) formula for area of a circle and of regular inscribed polygon,

(e) applications, interpretation of plans of land and houses, calculation of area from maps, scale (simple cases), problems involving buying land, etc.,

(f) construction of a square, equations such as $x^2 = 2$, square roots, examples of perfect squares, squaring and finding square root as inverses, square root tables for natural numbers (as an example of how tables can be constructed and used, rather than a means for finding square roots), finding a circle with a given area, equations of the type $ax^2 = b$,

(g) practical examples concerning prisms, pyramids, cylinders, construction of cardboard models, (the emphasis is on the underlying idea rather than on the calculations).

Volumes

(a) concept of volumes, intuitive notions, notion of equivalent solids,

(b) cuboids, volume in terms of a unit cube, revision of metric units, formula for volume of cuboid, cube of a number,

(c) right prisms, construction of models, intuitive deduction of volume of a right prism with a triangular base, intuitive generalisation of the formula to other right prisms and cylinders of revolution, pyramids and prisms with congruent bases and the same height (by experiment), volume of a pyramid and a cone of 'revolution' (to justify such terminology).

Secondary school (ages 12–18)

The syllabuses for secondary education are issued in documents which each deal with one grade (varying from 18 to 7 pages in length). These provide general objectives, preliminary remarks on methodology, suggestions for how much time should be allotted for each theme and topic (eg 7 periods on 'the addition, subtraction and multiplication of monomials and polynomials', and 6 on 'square roots of real numbers' (both in year 8 (13–14)). The syllabus for each topic is then spelled out in more detail. Thus, for example, on square roots:

'extraction of integer square roots of positive numbers (up to four digits with some justification of algorithm used). Approximate square roots, to at least one place of decimals, ..., use of tables of square roots'.

For space reasons all such details cannot be included. Below then we give themes, topics and suggested time allocation for the six years of secondary education (plus occasional elucidatory additional information).

An interesting feature of the Portuguese system is that the secondary school curriculum is offered as a night school curriculum for mature students. Lessons are given in the same school by the same teachers. The 'night school' provides a route to university.

Grade 7 (12–13)

I Questions of language 10 periods

(propositions, equivalent statements, truth and falsehood – exemplified through a variety of numerical examples (including, eg decomposition into prime factors, lcm, gcd) and set representation)

II Numbers
Integers (Z) 11 periods
Rationals (Q) 17 periods

(four operations, powers with natural exponents, introduction to monomials and polynomials)

III First degree equations with rational coefficients 10 periods
(algebraic treatment)

IV Mappings (functions) 12 periods
(concept, domain, codomain, images, direct and indirect proportionality, tables, applications, surjections, injections, bijections, arrow diagrams, cartesian graphs, $y = ax$, $y = ax + b$)

V Transformation geometry

Introduction	2 periods
Translations	12 periods

(vector properties, inverse, composition, applications to traditional Euclidean geometry eg equality of angles when a line intersects two parallel lines)

Rotations	4 periods

(central symmetry, examples of figures with rotational symmetry, composition of two rotations with the same centre)

Axial Symmetry	2 periods
Isometries in the plane	4 periods

(direct and indirect, two isometries compose to give an isometry)

VI Congruence of triangles 6 periods
(constructions making use of one or two isometries, constructing a triangle given three sides, etc.)

Grade 8 (13–14)

I	Equations and systems of equations	
	First order equations in one unknown	4 periods
	Addition, subtraction and multiplication of monomials and polynomials	7 periods
	Binomials as the product of factors, $(x \pm y)^2$ and $x^2 - y^2$	3 periods
	Equations with letters such as $ax + b = 0$	2 periods
	Systems of equations and problems	6 periods
	Factorization of polynomials and solution of $P(x) = 0$	8 periods
II	The reals (**R**)	2 periods
	Square roots	6 periods
	Errors, max and min values of an approximation	1 period
	Pythagoras' Theorem and irrationality	10 periods

(Pythagoras, irrationality of root 2, irrationals, difference in decimal expansions of rationals and irrationals, reference to irrationality of π , **R** as union of rationals and irrationals)

	Operations on **R**	2 periods
	Graph of $y = x^2$, solving $x^2 = k$	4 periods

III Further transformations (homotheties)
Introduction 7 periods
(revision of invariants under translations)

Scalar products of vectors 4 periods
(collinear vectors, experimental verification of defining properties of a vector space (eg $(a + b)u = au + bu$))

Homotheties 8 periods
(definition, invariants, scale–factors, direct and inverse homotheties ('enlargements' with a negative scale factor), applications (eg given two parallel segments AB and CD, determine a homothety which maps the first on the second)

IV Similarities
Definition, similar figures, classification of similarities 5 periods
Similar triangles 5 periods
(given two similar triangles, one can be mapped on the other by the composition of a homothety and an isometry)

Parallel projection and Thales' Theorem including proof) 2 periods
Further work on right–angled triangles 4 periods

Grade 9 (14–15)

I Order relations on **R** 13 periods
('less than' and 'greater than', the number line, modulus and absolute value, inequalities).

II Plane geometry 19 periods
(revision of results on angles, triangles, Pythagoras, symmetry and rotations; medians, angle bisector; circle, properties of radii and diameters, angle properties (an interesting 'historical' feature is that students are still introduced to the 'centesimal'

system of angle measure, as an alternative to the sexagesimal system which it failed to replace), circumscribed and inscribed circles for triangles, circumcentre and incentre)

III Exponents 5 periods
(powers with integer exponents, rules for calculation, standard (scientific) notation)

IV Roots 10 periods
($x^n = a$ ($n \in \mathbf{N}$, $a \in \mathbf{R}^+$) , possibility of more than one solution, nth roots , irrationality, finding approximate values, operations with roots, calculations with simple surds)

V Quadratic equations and applications 14 periods
VI Trigonometry 7 periods
(sine, cosine, tangent, cotangent for acute angles, use of tables (without need for interpolation), application to right-angled triangles)

VII 3-D geometry 16 periods
(various types of solids - prisms, pyramids, polyhedra, cylinders, cones; ideas of primitive terms (lines, points), axioms, theorems; simple properties, eg three non-collinear points define a plane; relative positions of lines and planes, use of models, necessary and sufficient conditions for a line to be parallel to a plane, etc. (without proof); angles between two lines, line and plane, perpendicular planes; surface areas and volumes of right prisms, regular pyramids, spheres, cylinders and cones of revolution).

Grade 10 (15-16)

In this grade the curriculum divides into five 'areas', one of which does not include mathematics. The curriculum below, therefore, applies to the remaining four areas. (The curriculum for this year is presented in a tabular form with headings 'Content', 'Methodological hints' and 'Objectives'.)

I Logic and algebra

1. Propositional logic 8 periods
(two-valued logic, law of excluded middle, negation, conjunction, disjunction, equivalence, properties (commutativity etc.), De Morgan's laws, contrapositive, converse, necessary and sufficient conditions)

2. Propositional expressions 4 periods
(equivalence of expressions, solution sets, applications to numbers and intervals, eg inequalities, equations and inequations)

3. Algebraic expressions 18 periods
(polynomials, operations on these, algorithm for division, remainder rule, Ruffini's rule (ie an algorithm for dividing polynomials using only coefficients), factorization, rational functions, algebraic fractions, surds)

4. Equations and inequations 5 periods
(solutions of equations such as $(ax + b)(cx^2 + d) = 0$, $[(ax + b)(cx + d)]/[(cx^2 + f)(gx + h)] = 0$, domains of algebraic expressions)

5. Linear systems of three equations in three unknowns 4 periods
(solution by substitution)

6. Formal implication 4 periods
(revision of ideas on necessary and sufficient, applications to inequalities and the solution of equations)

7. Quantifiers 4 periods
('for all', 'there exists', negation of expressions, truth or falsehood of propositions)

II Plane analytical geometry

1. Notions of trigonometry 17 periods
(radian measure, generalised trigonometric functions, $\sin^2\theta + \cos^2\theta = 1$, values of trigonometric functions for $30°$, $45°$, $60°$; trigonometric values of supplementary, complementary, negative angles, of $\theta + 90°$ and $\theta + 180°$, use of tables)

2. Vectors 8 periods
(tied and free vectors, length and direction, coordinates and components, orthonormal bases, collinearity, coordinates of a mid-point of a segment, distance between two points)

3. Scalar product 4 periods
(scalar product, orthogonal projection, commutativity)

4. Lines 10 periods

(determined by point and direction, vectorial equation, parametric representation, collinearity, perpendicular and parallel lines, intersection of two parallel lines, angle between two lines, angle bisectors, mediators)

5. Circles 6 periods
(vectorial equation, cartesian equation, condition for $ax^2 + by^2 + cx + dy + e = 0$ to represent a circle, determination of centre and radius, circle defined by three non-collinear points, intersection of line and circle, tangent)

6. Regions in the plane 3 periods
(half planes, open and closed regions, regions defined by inequalities such as $ax + by + c \leq 0$).

III Functions

1. Generalisations 8 periods
(restrictions and extensions, injections, surjections and bijections, equality of functions, inverse functions, composition of functions (associative but not commutative), inverse of a composite function, concept of a real function of a real variable, analytical definitions of functions, domains, zeros of a function, product and quotient of functions)

2. Trigonometric functions 5 periods
(periodicity, graphs of sine, cosine, tangent, simplification of expressions such as $\sin(\pi/2 - x) + \cos(5\pi + x) - \tan(x - 5\pi/2)$)

Grade 11 (16–17)

I Functions

1. Polynomials 10 periods
(linear functions and their properties, analytical and graphical study of quadratics, even and odd functions, graphs of polynomials of higher degree, domains, sum and product of roots of a quadratic, sketching, eg $(2 \mid x \mid /x)$)

2. Functions from **N** to **R** 8 periods
(sequences, definition of u_n or as a recurrence relation, monotonic sequences, bounded sequences, arithmetic and geometric progressions, sum of n consecutive terms)

II Elements of Analysis

1. Limit of a sequence 18 periods
(subsequence, convergent sequence, uniqueness of limit (with proof), constant sequences, subsequences tend to same limit, theorems on sum, product, difference, quotient, and on sequences of powers of terms of a convergent sequence, $u_n \rightarrow +\infty$, $u_n \rightarrow -\infty$, indeterminacy of '0/0' , '∞/∞' etc. intuitive study of (a^n) , sum of a geometric progression)

2. Exponential and Logarithmic functions 6 periods
(definitions of powers with rational and irrational exponents, intuitive study of $x \rightarrow a^x$ $(a > 0 , x \varepsilon \mathbf{R})$, graphs, definition of $\log_a x$, logarithms of product, quotient, powers, roots with natural indices, log as inverse of exp, domain, codomain, monotonicity, transforming of $a^b = c$ and $\log_a b = c$)

3. Limits of real functions of a real variable 12 periods
(points of accumulation, limit of $f(x)$ as x tends to a , extension to a as $+\infty$ or $-\infty$, theorem of uniqueness (with proof), limit of a constant function, one–sided limits, condition for a limit, Cauchy definition, theorems on sum, product, difference, quotient, powers, roots (proof for sums), study of limit of quotient when the divisor tends to 0 , indeterminacy of '0/0' etc. definition of continuous/discontinuous at a point, functions, continuous on a subset of their domain)

4. Differentiation
(derivative at a point and over an interval, geometric interpretation, examples from geometry, physics, etc, one–sided derivatives, differentiable implies continuous (with proof), derived function, theorems relating to sums, differences, products, powers and quotients of functions, derivative of inverse function, chain rule (composite functions), derivative of x^n and $x^{1/n}$, second and higher order derivatives, applications, asymptotes, maxima and minima, points of inflexion)

III Combinatorics and the Binomial Theorem

1. Combinatorics 10 periods
(number of injections from a set of cardinal p onto a set of cardinal n , permutations, number of bijections from a set of cardinal n to a set of cardinal n , factorial symbol ($n!$ for $n \varepsilon \mathbf{N}$) , combinations without repetitions, number of subsets of p elements of a set of cardinal n)

2. Binomial theorem (natural numbers) 2 periods

IV Introduction to statistics and probability

1. Statistics 8 periods
(statistical characteristics, frequencies, relative and cumulative, graphical and tabular representation, bar graphs, pie charts, pictograms, mode, median, mean, standard deviation, interpretation of parameters)

2. Probability 10 periods
(random phenomena, events, domain of the event, certain and impossible events, intersection of events; opposite and disjoint events, absolute frequency, experimental determination using relative frequencies, notion of probability obtained from relative frequency, axiomatisation of the concept of probability (finite space), determination of probability in cases of equally–likely and of non–equally–likely events, references to conditional and independent probability, problem of repeated trials)

Grade 12 (17–18)

Certain changes have recently been made to this syllabus. In particular, work on linear spaces is not now treated in school and the 9 periods given over to its teaching have been reallocated amongst the other themes.

1. Algebraic structure 8 periods
(notions of groupoid, semigroup, group, ring and field, examples, elementary properties, isomorphisms between groupoids, inverse composition of isomorphisms, reference to isomorphisms between rings)

2. The field of reals, **R** 8 periods
(axiomatic definition of the set of reals as an ordered, complete field, absolute value, properties and concept of 'supremum' and 'infimum', use of sigma notation for summation)

3. The complex numbers, **C** 12 periods
(definition of set of complex numbers, the 'mathematical proof' of **C** as a field, Argand diagram, trigonometric form, formulae for $\sin(a \pm b)$ and $\cos(a \pm b)$ (without proof), loci and regions defined by $|z - z_1| = |z - z_2|$, $|z - z_1| \leq 1$ etc, De Moivre)

4. Principle of Mathematical Induction 2 periods
$(1 + 3 + ... + (2n - 1) = n^2$, binomial theorem, $n^3 + 2n$ is divisible by 3, etc.)

5. Numerical sequences (A more formal treatment of work previously introduced) 12 periods
($\lim u_n \to a \Rightarrow \lim |u_n| \to |a|$, if $u_n \geq 0$ and (u_n) converges then $\lim u_n \geq 0$, (u_n) and (v_n) convergent and $u_n \leq v_n \Rightarrow \lim u_n \leq \lim v_n$, sandwich theorem, (a^n) , proof of $e^x = \lim (1 + {}^x/_n)^n$)

6. Real functions of a real variable 12 periods
('formal' review) (trigonometric formulae, $\sin \alpha - \sin \beta$ etc, intervals of **R** , open closed, interior, exterior, boundary, derived sets, continuity of functions, Theorems of Bolzano and Weierstrass, continuity of circular trigonometric functions, limit of $\sin x/x$ as $x \to 0$, inverse trig functions, exponential and logarithmic functions, various limits)

7. Differentiation 10 periods
(derivatives of circular trig functions and their inverses, exponential and logarithmic functions)

8. Rolle's and the mean–value theorems 8 periods

9. Graphs of real functions of a real variable 6 periods
('formal' review) (asymptotes, various examples)

10. Conics 8 periods
(geometrical definitions, cartesian equations, axes of symmetry, conics as planar sections of the surface of a cone)

The reform of the Portuguese school system has precipitated discussion about the form which the national curriculum might take in future and this has led to considerable activity amongst Portuguese teachers of mathematics. Out of this have emerged official proposals, of different levels of completeness, for reforming the syllabuses. We give a brief account of these below to illustrate present–day thought.

lst cycle (ages 6–10)

Here three main themes are suggested to be covered through activities, exploration, discovery and problems:

Numbers and operations

natural numbers, decimals, operations (mental and using aids)

Space and form

solids, geometrical figures, perimeter and area, transformations in the plane, use of instruments

Measure

notions of size, units of measure (including traditional ones) use of instruments and appliances.

2nd cycle (ages 10–12)

Here goals are spelled out in terms of attitudes and values, aptitudes (eg to analyse different components of a situation, to recognise analogies between different situations, etc.), and knowledge. Briefly the last comprises:

Grade 5

1. Geometrical solids (identification and properties of common polyhedra, cylinders, cones, construction of models)
2. Lines, polygons, circles (identification and classification, congruence)
3. Naturals and decimals (addition and subtraction of numbers and lengths)
4. Areas (metric units, formulae for rectangle and square, decomposition)
5. Integers and decimals (multiplication and division)
6. Statistics (organizing data, constructing and interpreting tables and graphs)
7. Fractions (representation by a quotient, comparison and ordering, decimal equivalents and conversion, addition and subtraction (including different denominators)
8. Lines in a plane (parallelism, perpendicularity)

9. Angles (right, acute, obtuse, drawing angles of a given size)

10. Triangles (classification, verifying angle sum)

11. Volumes (cube, cuboid, metric system)

Grade 6

1. Cylinders, perimeter of a circle (estimating π, circumference formula, net of cylinder (and surface area))

2. The four operations on the positive rationals (fractions and decimals, commutativity etc, brackets, applications)

3. Construction of triangles (SSS, SAS, ASA, ambiguous cases)

4. Quadrilaterals (parallelograms)

5. Symmetry in a line

6. Direct proportion

7. Statistics (tables and graphs, mean, use of calculator)

8. Areas (parallelogram, triangle, circle)

9. Integers (order, number line)

10. Addition and subtraction of integers

11. Volumes (prism, cylinder, experimental work).

3rd cycle (ages 12–15)

Here the syllabus is presented in a similar style to that for the 2nd cycle. Content topics are presented grade by grade under four general headings:

The reals (operations (mentally and with a calculator)), polynomials, solution of equations, inequations and simultaneous equations)
Functions (proportionality, inverse, representation by tables and graphically)

Statistics and probability (further examples of statistics in day to day life, notion and simple examples of probability)
Space (figures in the plane and space, congruence and similarity, geometrical constructions, use of instruments, errors of measurement and estimates, perimeters, areas and volumes, transformations of the plane (approached intuitively)).

Secondary (ages 15–18)

Official proposals for this cycle were published in Spring 1990. Content throughout the three grades is arranged under the four headings: Numbers and Algebra; Geometry and Trigonometry; Functions and Calculus; Statistics and Probability.

The content includes: basic statistics, but no sampling or hypothesis testing; probability up to the binomial and normal distributions; analytic geometry of lines, planes and conics; vector geometry up to scalar product; elementary combinatorics, ie permutations, combinations, and the binomial formula; sequences (APs, GPs, limits) and mathematical induction; trigonometry; systems of linear equations; the differential and integral calculus; exponential and logarithmic functions. Groups and fields are introduced in the final year and options include complex numbers, differential equations, linear spaces and transformation geometry.

SPAIN

Present system with school leaving age 14

Age (yr)	Grade		
5-6	K	Pre-school Education	
6-7	1	Elementary School	
7-8	2		
8-9	3		
9-10	4		
10-11	5		
11-12	6		
12-13	7		
13-14	8		
14-15	9	Bachillerato	Technical and Professional
15-16	10		
16-17	11		
17-18	12	Un. Orntn.	
18-19	13		

Notes

1. It is possible to enter university (or the university orientation year) from the advanced professional course (ie, at 19).

2. About 84% of four–year olds were in pre–school in 1985–86 and almost all five–year olds.

3. Recent figures for the distribution of students were:
total national population 39M,
primary (elementary) school students 5.6M,
secondary school students 2.24M,
vocational training students 738K,
university students 855K.

SPAIN

Proposed system with school-leaving age 16

Age (yr)	Grade		
5-6	K	Infant School	
6-7	1	Primary School	
7-8	2		
8-9	3		
9-10	4		
10-11	5		
11-12	6		
12-13	7	Secondary School	
13-14	8		
14-15	9		
15-16	10		
16-17	11	Bachillerato	Technical
17-18	12		

Notes

1. The model shown is expected to be fully effective in 1991.

2. Non–compulsory infant schools cover the age range 3–6. In these it is expected that mathematics will be introduced as a language to describe various numerical, quantitative and spatial entities and relations.

3. Five "bachillerato" are envisaged: Technical, Social Sciences, Natural Sciences, Arts, and Language and Letters.

SPAIN

Very great changes are currently taking place in Spanish education: the whole system is being redesigned and the school–leaving age (ie the age of compulsory attendance) raised from 14 to 16. The traditional 'elementary' school which catered for the eight years of compulsory education will be replaced by a six–year primary school followed by four years of comprehensive secondary school. The special courses leading to university education will become two years in length.

In preparation for the change there has been considerable planning including the formulation of new syllabuses. Traditionally, the basic syllabuses are fixed by the State. However, regions may make additions to these. The syllabuses described here are those for Catalonia, but are typical.

The primary syllabuses have, in fact, not been subject to many changes for they were revised comparatively recently. Two principles have, however, been given special emphasis: (i) the need to make mathematics learning significant – to take into account what is known and also what is important; and (ii) the need to have periodic reviews of concepts and methods in order that these can be approached and understood at ever–increasing levels of complexity, abstraction and formality.

The syllabus itself is presented in a very detailed form: it begins with 20 pages of general introduction, after which five general objectives are set out (the identification of situations susceptible to mathematical analysis; the utilisation of the principal systems of numeration; a knowledge of measure; identification of 'real–life' situations and problems which can be solved by arithmetic and simple numerical algorithms; and the use of calculating (pocket calculator, abacus,...) and measuring (ruler, compasses,...) instruments). Thirty pages on content are then presented under three headings: 'Facts, concepts and principles', 'Procedures and algorithms' and 'Attitudes, values and norms'. The material is divided into five blocks: Numbers, Measure, Space, Shapes and Statistics. Below we give a summary of the contents of all three sections relating to number, and a brief description only of the 'facts' sections for the four remaining blocks. The printed 'syllabus' concludes with 20 or so pages on pedagogical matters including advice on evaluation.

No attempt is made to legislate for the order in which material is to be taught or on what material is to be covered in any one year.

Primary school (Grades 1–6, ages 6–12)

1. NUMBERS AND OPERATIONS: MEANING AND STRATEGIES

Facts, concepts and principles

1. natural numbers, integers, fractions and decimals (including motivating needs, relations between numbers (>, <, =, ≥, ≤, ≈) , simple fractions and their decimal representation, percentage);

2. systems of numeration (decimal, roman, money, angles, time) (numerals, base, position, rules, ±, cardinals and ordinals);

3. operations of addition, subtraction, multiplication and division (operations and their uses in different situations; squares and cubes, inverse operations, symbols);

4. correspondences between language, graphic representation and numerical notation;

5. algorithms of the four operations (including rules for using a calculator);

Procedures

1. use of different strategies for counting in exact form and in approximate form;

2. relations between natural numbers, decimal numbers (with two decimal places) and simple fractions: order, graphical representation and transformations;

3. interpretation of numerical tables and alphanumerical tables (operations, time tables, prices, bills, ... etc.) which are met in real life;

4. making and using different codes in order to represent objects, situations, events and actions;

5. use of the decimal system of numeration;

6. use of the money system;

7. interpretation, computation and relations of percentage;

8. formulating and verifying conjectures of a numerical nature;

9. use of strategies for solving numerical problems;

10. expressing computations and problems verbally;

11. mathematical representation of some situations by means of different languages (verbal, graphic, numerical) and relating their outcomes;

12. deciding on the convenience or not of making exact or approximate computations and evaluating the degree of error introduced;

13. estimating the result of a computation and deciding if a numerical answer is acceptable or not;

14. automatic use of the algorithms for the four basic equations on whole numbers;

15. automatic use of the algorithms for addition and subtraction of decimal numbers with two digits and for fractions with the same denominators;

16. formulation of personal strategies for mental computation;

17. identification of daily problems where the basic operations play a role;

18. use of the calculator for the four operations and decisions on the convenience of its use bearing in mind the complexity of the computations to be made and the needs of exactness.

Attitudes, values and norms

1. curiosity for searching and exploring the meaning of numerical and alphanumerical codes, their regularities and the relations which appear in numerical sets;

2. sensibility for and interest in information and messages of a numerical nature; appreciating the utility of numbers in real–life;

3. rigour in the precise use of numerical symbols; knowledge of the rules of

the different systems of numbers and interest in knowing alternative strategies;

4. tenacity and perseverance in searching for solutions to a problem;

5. confidence in personal capacities and in devising personal strategies for mental computations;

6. appreciating orderly and clear presentation of computations and their results;

7. confidence in and critical attitudes towards the use of the calculator.

2. MEASURE: QUANTITATIVE INFORMATION ON OBJECTS AND TIME

Facts, concepts and principles

1. the need for, and functions of, measuring;

2. perimeter, area and volume of figures as expressions (quantitative) of their size;

3. the units of measure in the metric system (length, area, capacity, mass);

4. local units of measure;

5. the units of measure for time;

6. the unit of measure for angles; the degree.

3. REPRESENTATION AND ORGANIZATION IN SPACE

Facts, concepts and principles

1. points and reference systems (including distances, angles, cartesian references,...);

2. geometrical elements (including parallelism, orthogonality, intersections,...);

3. elementary representations of space (plans, maps, models, scales, graphical scales,...);

4. instruments for drawing (ruler, compasses,...).

4. SHAPES IN SPACE

Facts, concepts and principles

1. 2–D shapes (figures, polygons, circumference, relations, regularities, symmetries, sum of the angles of a triangle);

2. 3–D shapes (bodies with vertices, edges and faces, cube, sphere, prism, pyramid, cone, cylinder; relations in a cube, regularities...);

5. ORGANIZATION OF INFORMATION: GRAPHICS AND AN INTRODUCTION TO STATISTICS

Facts, concepts and principles

1. graphical representation (characteristics, uses, different statistical graphs);

2. frequency tables;

3. arithmetical mean and mode.

The Secondary School

Particular attention has, of course, been paid to the new secondary school curriculum, for that had to be constructed effectively from scratch. Because of this newness it has been necessary to spell out the objectives of the course in considerable detail and to make lengthy observations on methodology and means of assessment. In particular, these parts of the 'national curriculum' give considerable attention to process objectives and, indeed, the aims of mathematics–for–all, 12–16. Three hours per week are allocated to mathematics throughout these years. In addition to the compulsory course, schools may offer optional mathematics courses.

The actual syllabus content is presented in five blocks: Numbers and operations; Measure; Representation and organization in space; Interpretation, representation and treatment of information; Chance. The material within each block is not allotted to specific years. (The system used, then, resembles that of, say, Italy.) In practice, curricular treatment will depend very much upon the textbooks which are produced to cover the syllabus.

1. NUMBERS AND OPERATIONS

The main emphasis is on the various types of numbers, operations and methods of calculation, and an understanding of the appropriateness of particular operations for the solution of problems. Various methods of calculating are developed (mental, written, using instruments, exact, approximate,...) and their appropriateness considered. The links with other blocks, eg geometry, probability, are stressed.

Facts, concepts and principles

(1) natural numbers, integers, decimals and fractions (including percentages and scientific notation);

(2) operations (significance and use of the four operations in various contexts and different number sets; powers and square roots);

(3) relations between numbers (order and representation on the number line; multiple/divisor relation);

(4) proportionality of magnitudes (significance of proportion in different contexts);

(5) approximation and estimation of quantities (including likely errors);

(6) basic algorithms and means of calculation (algorithms for operations on integers, decimals and fractions; conventions for order of operations, brackets; commutativity, associativity, distributivity and their use in strategies for calculation; use of calculators and other instruments);

(7) algebraic language (significance and use of letters for representing numbers – unknowns, variables; relations between sets of numbers; formulae and equations; simplification of algebraic expressions).

PROCEDURES

(1) use of numbers, operations and algebraic language in different contexts selection of most appropriate means;

(2) interpretation and construction of codes and numerical tables;

(3) diagrammatic representation including number line;

(4) oral formulation of algebraic and numerical problems leading to their solution.

Algorithms and competencies

(5) comparison of numbers by means of order, graphical representation and the computation of percentages;

(6) classification of sets of numbers and construction of a sequence according to a given rule;

(7) approximation by substitution of simpler numbers;

(8) mental arithmetic with simple numbers;

(9) use of operations and rules for order, parentheses etc. in written computations;

(10) use of traditional algorithms for the four operations on integers, decimals and fractions;

(11) use of different procedures (eg decimal to fraction and vice versa) to simplify computations;

(12) use of different procedures relating to proportionality;

(13) use of the calculator and other instruments bearing in mind the accuracy required;

(14) use of algorithms to solve linear equations in one unknown – and numerical and graphical means for finding approximate solutions of other equations.

General strategies

(15) use of various strategies for counting and estimation, precision;

(16) searching for properties, relations and regularities in sets of numbers;

(17) identifying knowns and unknowns in a numerical problem and deciding which are relevant to its solution;

(18) identification of uses of proportionality in real life (specific terminology, eg ratios, interest,...);

(19) reduction of complex numerical problems to simpler ones in order to facilitate understanding a solution;

(20) decisions on the appropriate operations needed to solve a numerical problem;

(21) making conjectures on numerical situations and problems, using examples and counter-examples;

(22) use of arithmetic reasoning or working backwards to solve problems.

ATTITUDES, VALUES AND NORMS

References to the appreciation of mathematics

(1) appreciating the precision, simplicity and utility of numerical and algebraic languages to represent, communicate and solve real-life situations;

(2) using numerical language and calculations in day-to-day living;

(3) appreciating and criticising information of a numerical nature;

(4) recognition and critical evaluation of the utility of the calculator and other instruments for computation;

(5) curiosity and interest to tackle numerical problems and to search for problems and relations appearing in numerical sets or codes;

(6) confidence in a personal capacity to face problems requiring computations and estimations.

References to organization and work habits

(7) tenacity and perseverance in searching for solutions to numerical problems and in making improvements;

(8) systematically reviewing results;

(9) flexibility in considering numerical situations from different viewpoints;

(10) interest in and respect for the strategies and solutions of others;

(11) appreciating orderly and clear presentations of procedures and results.

A similar approach is adopted for the other four 'blocks', but for space reasons we give below only the 'facts, concepts and principles' sections of these.

2. MEASURE

(1) measures of magnitudes – length, area, volume, time, units;

(2) systems of measurement – metric system, astronomical measures, traditional weights and measures;

(3) measures of time – including those in other cultures;

(4) angle measure – in the plane and between two planes;

(5) approximate measures – estimation, approximation errors;

(6) indirect measures – eg use of similarity, formulae for perimeters, areas and volumes of geometrical shapes in two and three dimensions, Pythagoras' theorem;

(7) measuring instruments – popular current and traditional instruments, high precision instruments.

3. REPRESENTATION AND ORGANIZATION IN SPACE

(1) Geometric elements in 2– and 3–D – points, lines, planes, parallel, perpendicular and coordinates;

(2) 2– and 3–D shapes – classification, characteristic elements of polygons and conics, of polyhedra, sphere, cone, cylinder etc., relations, regularities and symmetries; utility and importance of shapes for concrete purposes (eg minimizing area etc);

(3) similar figures and scales – maps and models, characteristics of two

congruent shapes, Thales' Theorem, relations between length, area and volume of similar figures;

(4) geometric transformations – translations, rotations, reflections; invariant properties and composition.

4. INTERPRETATION, REPRESENTATION AND TREATMENT OF INFORMATION

(1) information on deterministic phenomena – cartesian graphs to represent relations and changes between two magnitudes, global characteristics of graphs (continuity, monotonicity, extreme values), linear, quadratic, exponential and periodic phenomena and graphs, the meaning of a linear graph in terms of proportion, algebraic representation;

(2) information on random phenomena – obtaining data on random phenomena, tabular and graphical representation, parameters (means and standard deviation), algorithms to calculate mean value and standard deviation in easy cases, statistical dependence of variables.

5. CHANCE

(1) random phenomena and terminology to describe them – experiments on random phenomena, regularities in large samples, possibility of an event occurring;

(2) assigning probabilities to events – frequencies and probability of an event, Laplace's rule;

(3) assigning probabilities to combined events – dependence and independence, conditional probability.

The syllabuses for the later years of education within the new system have still to be determined. At the moment experimentation is taking place and a number of proposals are under consideration.

Below, therefore, we give a brief indication of the content of the syllabuses currently in use for secondary education, ie for the cycle 14–18 (3 years Bachillerato plus one year of the preparatory course for university).

Grade 9 (age 14–15)

Numbers: naturals, integers, rationals – introduction to real and complex numbers;
Basic concepts in combinatorics;
Probability and statistics: data, parameters, events, normal distribution, regression;
Polynomials in one unknown and rational functions, graphs;
Linear equations, inequalities, systems of both, applications;
APs and GPs with applications.

Grade 10 (age 15–16)

Classical coordinate geometry, vectors in the plane, lines and planes;
Trigonometry: basic definitions, relations and applications;
Sequences of real numbers and their limits, e ;
Real functions, study of functions, limits, exp, log, sin, cos, tan;
Derivatives, concepts, computation, primitive functions.

Grade 11 (age 16–17)

Geometry: inner (scalar) product and metric concepts, conics;
Trigonometry: formulae and theorems, solution of triangles, applications;
Complex numbers: representations, powers and roots;
Derivatives and integrals, graph sketching, computations, areas;
Statistics: random variable, distributions.

Grade 12 (age 17–18, university orientation year)

The emphasis and content here differs, depending upon whether or not the student is taking Maths I (science students) or Maths II (non–science students). The key content is:

Geometry of the plane and space, matrices, systems of equations, Gauss' method;
Analysis (real function of a single real variable); derivatives, integrals, graphs;
Statistics and probability.

THE UNITED KINGDOM

ENGLAND AND WALES

(See below for brief notes on Northern Ireland and Scotland)

Age (yr)	Grade	
5-6	K	Primary School
6-7	1	
7-8	2	
8-9	3	
9-10	4	
10-11	5	
11-12	6	Secondary School (Comprehensive)
12-13	7	
13-14	8	
14-15	9	
15-16	10	
16-17	11	Sixth Form
17-18	12	

Notes

1. Various other structures can be found within the system. In particular:

(a) in some areas children from 8–12, or from 9–13, attend "middle schools"; in others, secondary education is still differentiated by school–type: at 11+ students attend either a grammar school or a secondary modern/comprehensive school (but both types of school follow the same national curriculum),

(b) sixth–form education can be provided by 11–18 or 13–18 schools, by specialist "sixth form colleges", or by "colleges of further education" (which also provide vocational courses).

2. Independent schools are not bound by the national curriculum and testing at 7, 11 and 14. However, an external examination system at 16 shared with the state schools ensures a considerable degree of uniformity within mathematics teaching.

3. Pre–school education is not well developed in England and Wales. Private provision exists for child–care and play–groups. It is intended to develop such state provision as exists, but no detailed plans have been set out.

THE UNITED KINGDOM

There is no single educational system for the UK; each of England, Northern Ireland, Scotland and Wales has its own education office (or ministry) and its own traditions.

Thus, primary school in Northern Ireland begins at age 4, as against age 5 in England, Scotland and Wales, and from 11+ schooling is bipartite. In Scotland, secondary education has traditionally begun at 12 (at 11 in the other three systems) and students have entered university at 17 (18) and have studied there for 4 years (3). The major centres in Scotland had universities several centuries before alternatives to Oxford and Cambridge were created in England; again, elementary schooling was provided publicly in Scotland well before it was in England. These different Scottish educational traditions would still seem to affect the percentages of students staying on at school post–16 and proceeding to higher education.

A 'national' primary/elementary educational system was not established in England until the late 19th century, and secondary education was first provided by the state in the early years of the 20th century. Before then, schools had been provided by religious bodies, guilds of tradesmen, charitable foundations, private individuals, etc. When a national educational system was created, it was of a very heterogeneous nature. Opposition to a state–controlled curriculum resulted in considerable local and school autonomy, although external examinations at 16 and 18 have increasingly ensured a large degree of uniformity at the secondary level. In particular, the 'independent' or private sector of education retains a social and political influence out of proportion to its size. Curricular autonomy is still a feature of UK universities and polytechnics and this has an influence on upper secondary school curricula.

Since the 1970s the majority of children have attended comprehensive schools. Before that, there was a tripartite system of grammar, technical and "modern" schools. Even within the 11–16 comprehensive schools there is differentiation of mathematics syllabuses. One way in which this is currently achieved for many pupils is through three 'nested' curricula leading to four graded examination papers, with any student opting for two, ie, 1+2 , 2+3 or 3+4.

Recent governments have demonstrated a desire to bring greater uniformity to an educational system which, for a variety of reasons (many of which arise from outside the classroom), underperforms in certain important respects (eg, average attainment of pupils in the lower half of the range, and post–16 retention rates) relative to the systems of countries viewed as industrial and commercial competitors.

The most recent result is the Education Reform Act of 1988 which established a National Curriculum for state schools (not binding on independent schools) for the age range 5–16 and decreed that children's attainment should be tested (in externally–directed ways) at 7, 11, 14 and 16 (but see below for Northern Ireland).

The timetable for the implementation of the changes was directed by political rather than educational considerations. England and Wales were the first to produce proposals for mathematics and they began to take effect from 1989. Northern Ireland followed a year later. Scotland is not covered by the Education Reform Act.

Here we have space only for a description of the 5–16 National Curriculum shared by England and Wales. Note, however, that children in Wales have by law to study one more subject, namely Welsh, than their peers in England. It would have proved difficult then to have allocated timetabled hours for subjects in a sensible, consistent manner. It is stipulated, therefore, that all compulsory subjects (including mathematics) must be taught for a 'reasonable amount of time' – 'reasonable' being nowhere defined. (It is recommended that ten per cent of the week should be devoted to mathematics in Grades 9 and 10.)

The structure devised for the curriculum and testing may be best described as 'unique'. The need for differentiation of presentation was accepted, but streaming is not built into the curriculum; rather all pupils (even in those parts of the country still retaining a bipartite or tripartite system) are to follow the same curriculum, presented in each subject at 10 levels, at their own pace but, usually, with automatic promotion from class to class. The general assumptions concerning learning patterns, spread of attainment, etc. are given in the graph overleaf.

In theory (ie in statements from governmental agencies), the National Curriculum comprises:

'Attainment targets, to be specified at up to 10 levels of attainment';

programmes of study setting out 'matters, skills and processes which have to be taught to pupils ... in order for them to meet the objectives set out in attainment targets';

'assessment arrangements related to the 10 levels of attainment'.

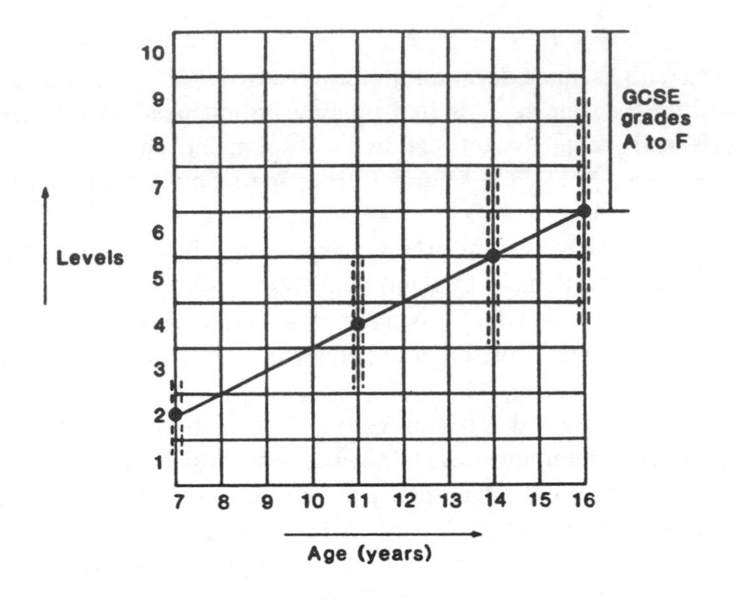

Figure 1 Sequence of pupil achievement of levels between ages 7 and 16

(The bold line gives the expected results for pupils at the ages specified. The dotted lines represent a rough speculation on the limits within which about 80% of the pupils may be found to lie.)

The structure is, indeed, extremely complicated. It is hoped the following notes will convey something of its nature.

(I) Mathematics has been divided into 14 attainment targets (13 in NI), eg, 'Pupils should understand number and number notations' (AT2) and 'Pupils should use graphical representation of algebraic functions' (AT7), most having 10 levels (but, eg, AT7 has no 'Levels' 1–3). A teacher will be expected to know at which level in each attainment target, each of the pupils in the class is performing. (The impracticability of the proposals is now being recognised officially. In January, 1991, it was announced that the number of attainment targets in mathematics will be reduced, as will the number of subjects to be compulsorily studied at Key Stage 4. Mathematics, however, remains compulsory and no changes to the actual mathematics curriculum, as distinct from assessment procedures, are currently promised.)

(II) Pupils will [in theory] work through the levels at their own pace, gradually attaining the various levels (though what it means to 'attain' a level has still to be defined).

(III) Four 'key stages' have been established:

Key Stage			
1	ages 5–7	(4–8 in NI)
2	ages 7–11	(8–11 in NI)
3	ages 11–14	
4	ages 14–16.	

There will be an assessment programme for each key stage.

(IV) 'Pupils at age 14 [as an example], though typically achieving at around levels 4 to 7, might show attainment at anything from level 3 to level 8'. Accordingly, a variety of levels will need to be taught to different pupils at each key stage:

Key Stage	Levels
1	1–3 (effective from 1989)
2	2–6 (effective from 1990)
3	3–8 (effective from 1989)
4	4–10 (effective from 1992)

(These 'expected' levels are exactly the same for NI, although we note that there Key Stage 1 begins one year earlier and ends one year later).

(V) In E and W the 'programmes of study' are (to quote the NI report) 'merely the transpose of the attainment target matrix'. They, therefore, supply no new information or help to the teacher. (The NI proposals begin with radically different 'programmes of study', but then offer statements of attainment which do not differ greatly from those of E and W. Thus, in NI, programmes of study are given by key stages (ie they look very much like the syllabuses of other countries), but the English matrix of attainment targets is mainly preserved. Some changes have been made for what the author regards as the better, others have been made for (to him) no obvious reason, eg "know that $2^5 = 2 \times 2 \times 2 \times 2 \times 2$", is Level 7 in NI (and so not necessarily expected of the average student of 16+), whereas it is Level 5 in E and W.)

(VI) Teachers, textbook authors and others still await information on the 'assessment arrangements'.

Since the programmes of study and attainment targets are effectively transposes of each other, we shall need to give only one of these. We reprint the programmes of study for the various levels. The 14 attainment targets are obtained by subdividing 'Number' into three parts, 'Algebra' into three, 'Shape and Space' into two, 'Handling data' into three, and repeating 'Using and applying mathematics' – once with respect to number, measure and algebra, once with respect to shape and size, and handling data. (NI lose one AT by taking the view that one 'uses and applies mathematics' without subdivisions.)

Already, as indicated above, the Government is beginning to think again about this elaborate and unworkable system. Pupils in Key Stage 1 in England will now only be assessed in English, mathematics and science: the detailed timetable for examining other subjects has been scrapped. Other changes will doubtless follow.

Programmes of study for the years 5–16

(Note: any children beginning primary education before age 5 begin at Level 1.)

Each level is preceded by the statement that to achieve that level students should be performing as indicated below.

LEVEL 1

Using and applying mathematics: using materials for a practical task, talking about own work and asking questions, making predictions based on experience.

Number: counting, reading, writing and ordering numbers to at least 10, understanding conservation of number, using addition and subtraction with numbers no greater than 10 in the context of real objects, making a sensible estimation of a number of objects up to 10.

Algebra: copying, continuing and devising repeating patterns.

Measures: comparing and ordering objects without measuring, using appropriate language.

Shape and space: sorting and classifying 2–D and 3–D shapes, building 3–D solid shapes and drawing 2–D shapes and describing them, using common words to describe a position, giving and understanding instructions for movement along a line.

Handling data: selecting criteria for sorting a set of objects, and applying them consistently, recording with objects or drawing, creating simple mapping diagrams showing relationships and interpreting them, recognising possible outcomes of random events.

LEVEL 2 (Median pupil attains at 7)

Using and applying mathematics: selecting the materials and the mathematics to use for a practical task, describing work and checking results, asking and responding to the question: "What would happen if...?"

Number: reading, writing and ordering numbers to at least 100 and using the knowledge that the tens digit indicates the number of tens, understanding the meaning of "half" and "quarter", knowing and using addition and subtraction facts up to 10, comparing two numbers to find the difference, solving whole number problems involving addition and subtraction, including money, making a sensible estimate of a number of objects up to 20.

Algebra: exploring and using patterns in addition and subtraction facts to 10, distinguishing odd and even numbers, understanding the use of a symbol to stand for an unknown number.

Measures: using non–standard measures in length, area, volume, capacity, "weight" and time, comparing objects and recognising the need for standard units, using coins in simple contexts, knowing commonly used units in length, capacity, "weight" and time.

Shape and space: recognising squares, rectangles, circles, triangles, hexagons, pentagons, cubes, rectangular boxes (cuboids), cylinders and spheres and describing them, understanding the notion of angle, understanding turning through right–angles and recognising right–angled corners, recognising types of movement: straight (translation), turning (rotation) and flip (reflection).

Handling data: choosing criteria to sort and classify objects; recording results or outcomes of events, designing a data collection sheet, recording data leading to a frequency table, constructing and interpreting frequency tables and block graphs, using diagrams to represent the result of classification using two different criteria, recognising a degree of uncertainty about the outcomes of some events and that other events are certain or impossible.

LEVEL 3 (Median pupil attains at 9)

Using and applying mathematics: selecting the materials and the mathematics to use for a task, checking results, considering whether they are sensible, explaining work and recording findings systematically, making and testing predictions.

Number: reading, writing and ordering numbers to at least 1000, and using the knowledge that the position of a digit indicates its value, using decimal notation in recording money, appreciating the meaning of negative whole numbers in familiar contexts, e.g. a temperature scale, knowing and using addition and subtraction facts to 20 (including zero), solving problems involving multiplication or division of whole numbers or money, using a calculator where necessary, knowing and using multiplication facts up to 5×5 and all those in 2, 5 and 10 multiplication tables, recognising the first digit is the most important in indicating the size of a number, and approximating to the nearest 10 or 100, understanding remainders and knowing whether to round up or down.

Algebra: finding number patterns and equivalent forms of 2–digit numbers and using these to perform mental calculations, explaining number patterns and predicting subsequent numbers, recognising whole numbers divisible by 2, 5 and 10, dealing with inputs to and outputs from simple function machines.

Measures: using a wider range of metric units, choosing and using appropriate units and instruments, interpreting numbers on a range of measuring instruments, making estimates based on familiar units.

Shape and space: sorting 2–D and 3–D shapes and giving reasons, recognising (reflective) symmetry in a variety of shapes in 2 and 3 dimensions, using and understanding compass bearings and the terms "clockwise" and "anti–clockwise".

Handling data: extracting information from tables and lists, entering and accessing information in a simple database, constructing and interpreting bar charts and graphs (pictograms) where the symbol represents a group of units, placing events in order of "likelihood" and using appropriate words to identify the chance, understanding and using the idea of "evens", distinguishing "fair" and "unfair".

LEVEL 4 (Median pupil attains at 11)

Using and applying mathematics: selecting the materials and the mathematics to use for a task and planning work methodically, recording findings and presenting them in oral, written or visual form, using examples to test statements or definitions.

Number: reading, writing and ordering whole numbers, understanding and using the effect of multiplying whole numbers by 10 or 100, using, with understanding, decimal notation to two decimal places in the context of measurement, understanding and using relationship between place values in whole numbers, recognising and understanding simple fractions, recognising and understanding simple percentages, knowing multiplication facts up to 10 × 10 and using them in multiplication and division problems, adding and subtracting mentally two 2–digit numbers, adding [sic] mentally single–digit numbers, adding and subtracting two 3–digit numbers without a calculator, multiplying and dividing 2–digit numbers by a single–digit number without a calculator, estimating and approximating to check the validity of addition and subtraction calculations, reading calculator displays to the nearest whole number and knowing how to interpret results which have rounding errors, solving addition and subtraction problems using numbers with no more than two decimal places, and multiplication and division problems starting with whole numbers.

Algebra: exploring properties of numbers including equivalence of fractions, generalising patterns, e.g. symmetry of results, understanding and using simple formulae or equations expressed in words, recognising that multiplication and division are inverse operations and using this to check calculations, knowing the conventions of the coordinate representation of points, working with coordinates in the first quadrant.

Measures: understanding the relationship between units, finding areas by counting squares, and volumes by counting cubes, making sensible estimates of a range of measures in relation to everyday objects.

Shape and space: understanding and using language associated with angle, constructing 2–D and 3–D shapes from given information, specifying location by means of coordinates in the first quadrant and by means of angle and distance, recognising rotational symmetry.

Handling data: specifying an issue for which data are needed, collecting and grouping discrete data, using frequency tables and block graphs with suitable equal class intervals, understanding, calculating and using the mean and range of a set of data, interrogating data in a computer database, constructing and interpreting bar–

line and line graphs and frequency diagrams with suitable class intervals for discrete variables, creating a decision–tree diagram, understanding and using probability scale from 0 to 1, giving and justifying subjective estimates of probabilities, listing all the possible outcomes of an event.

LEVEL 5 (Median pupil attains at 13)

Using and applying mathematics: selecting the materials and the mathematics to use for a task, checking there is sufficient information, working methodically and reviewing progress, interpreting mathematical information presented in oral, written or visual form, making and testing simple statements.

Number: using index notation to express powers of whole numbers, using unitary ratios, understanding and using non–calculator methods by which a 3–digit number is multiplied by a 2–digit number and a 3–digit number is divided by a 2–digit number, calculating fractions and percentages of quantities, multiplying and dividing mentally single–digit multiples of powers of 10, using negative numbers in context, using 'trial and improvement' methods and refining, approximating, using significant figures or decimal places.

Algebra: understanding and using terms such as "prime", "square", "cube", "square root", "cube root", "multiple" and "factor", generating sequences, recognising patterns in numbers through spatial arrangements, understanding and using simple formulae or equations expressed in symbolic form, expressing simple functions symbolically, understanding and using coordinates in all four quadrants.

Measures: understanding the notion of scale in maps and drawings, using imperial units still in daily use and knowing their rough metric equivalents, converting one metric unit to another, measuring and drawing angles to the nearest degree.

Shape and space: understanding congruence of simple shapes, using properties associated with intersecting and parallel lines and triangles and knowing associated language, identifying the symmetries of various shapes, using networks to solve problems, specifying location by means of coordinates in four quadrants.

Handling data: designing and using an observation sheet to collect data, collating and analyzing results, collecting and grouping continuous data and creating frequency tables, inserting and interrogating data in a computer database and drawing conclusions, constructing and interpreting pie charts from a collection of data with a few variables, constructing and interpreting conversion graphs, constructing and interpreting frequency diagrams and choosing class intervals for a continuous variable, distinguishing between estimates of probabilities based on statistical evidence and those based on assumptions of symmetry, knowing that if each of n events is assumed to be equally likely, the probability of one occurring is 1/n, knowing that different outcomes may result from repeating an experiment.

LEVEL 6 (Median pupil attains at 15)

Using and applying mathematics: designing a task and selecting the mathematics and resources, checking information and obtaining any that is missing , using "trial and improvement" methods, presenting findings using oral, written or visual forms, making and testing generalisations and simple hypotheses, defining and reasoning with some precision.

Number: reading, writing and ordering decimals and appreciating place values, understanding and using equivalence of fractions and ratios, working out fractional and percentage changes, calculating using ratios in a variety of situations, converting fractions to decimals and percentages, using estimation and approximation to check that answers to multiplication and division problems involving whole numbers are of the right order.

Algebra: determining possible rules for generating sequences, using spreadsheets or other computer facilities to explore number patterns, solving linear equations; solving simple polynomial equations by "trial and improvement" methods, using and plotting Cartesian coordinates to represent simple function mappings.

Measures: understanding and using compound measures, e.g. speed, density, recognising that measurement is approximate and choosing the degree of accuracy required for a particular purpose.

Shape and space: classifying and defining types of quadrilaterals, using angle and symmetry properties of quadrilaterals and polygons, using 2–D representation of 3–D objects, using computers to generate and transform 2–D shapes, understanding and using bearings to define direction, reflecting simple shapes in a mirror line, enlarging a shape by a whole number scale factor, devising instructions for a computer to produce desired shapes and paths.

Handling data: designing and using observation sheets, collating and analysing results, surveying opinions, using a questionnaire (taking account of bias), creating scatter graphs for discrete and continuous variables, constructing and interpreting information through two–way tables and network diagrams, identifying outcomes of two combined events which are independent, knowing that the total sum of the probabilities of mutually exclusive events is 1 and that the probability of something happening is 1 minus the probability of it not happening.

LEVEL 7 (Not expected to be completed by median pupil at 16)

Using and applying mathematics: devising a mathematical task, working methodically within an agreed structure, using judgement, "trial and improvement" methods and reviewing progress, following a chain of mathematical reasoning, spotting inconsistencies, following new lines of investigation using alternative methods to overcome difficulties.

Number: expressing positive integers as a product of primes, multiplying and dividing mentally single–digit multiples of any power of 10, solving problems using multiplication and division with numbers of any size, using memory and bracket facility of a calculator to plan a calculation and evaluate expressions.

Algebra: using symbolic notation to express the rules of sequences, understanding the meaning of reciprocals and exploring relationships, exploring complex number patterns generated by a computer, using the rules of indices for positive integer values, solving simple inequalities on a number line, solving a range of polynomial equations by "trial and improvement" methods, using algebraic methods to solve simultaneous linear equations in two variables, drawing and interpreting the graphs of linear functions and using graphical methods to solve simultaneous linear equations, generating various types of graphs on a computer or calculator and interpreting them.

Measures: recognising the possible error in a measurement.

Shape and space: understanding and applying Pythagoras' Theorem, determining locus of an object moving subject to a rule, enlarging a shape by a fractional scale factor, using coordinates to locate position in 3–D.

Handling data: specifying and testing a simple hypothesis, using and recording grouped data with class intervals suitably defined, producing a frequency table, calculating the mean using a calculator, finding the mean, median, mode and range of a frequency distribution for given sets of data and interpreting results, drawing a frequency polygon as a line graph from a frequency distribution for grouped data, constructing and interpreting flow diagrams with and without loops, drawing a line of "best fit" by inspection on a scatter diagram, understanding and using relative frequency as an estimate of probability, when assigning probabilities appreciating that relative frequency and equally likely considerations may not be appropriate and that "subjective" estimates of probability have to be made, understanding and applying the addition of probabilities for mutually exclusive events.

LEVEL 8

Using and applying mathematics: devising a mathematical task and making a detailed plan of the work, working methodically, checking information, considering whether results are of the right order, making statements of conjecture using "if... then...", defining, reasoning, proving and disproving.

Number: using index notations to represent powers and roots, expressing and using numbers in standard index form, with positive and negative integer powers of 10, substituting negative numbers into formulae, calculating with fractions, estimating and approximating to check that the results of calculations are of the right order.

Algebra: understanding the role of counter–example in the context of rules for sequences and in disproving hypotheses, understanding the relationships between powers and roots, solving a variety of linear and other inequalities, using a range of formulae and functions, manipulating simple algebraic expressions, knowing the form of graphs of quadratic functions and simple reciprocal functions, using straight line graphs to locate regions given by linear inequalities.

Measures: using knowledge and skills in length, area and volume to carry out calculations in plane and solid shapes, distinguishing between formulae for perimeter, area and volume by considering dimensions.

Shape and space: using sine, cosine and tangent in right–angled triangles in two dimensions, understanding and using mathematical similarity, understanding and using vector notation.

Handling data: designing and using a questionnaire with multiple responses, collating and analysing results to test a hypothesis, constructing a cumulative frequency table, constructing a cumulative frequency curve using the upper boundary of the class interval, finding the median, upper quartile, lower quartile and interquartile range, and interpreting the results, understanding that when dealing with two independent events, the probability of them both happening is less than the probability of either of them happening (unless the probability is 0 or 1), calculating the probability of a combined event given the probability of two independent events and illustrating combined probabilities of several events using tabulation or tree–diagrams.

LEVEL 9

Using and applying mathematics: designing, planning and carrying through a mathematical task to a successful conclusion, stating whether a conjecture is true, false or not proven, defining and reasoning, proving and disproving and using counter–examples, using symbolisation, recognising and using necessary and sufficient conditions.

Number: distinguishing between rational and irrational numbers, being aware of upper and lower bounds of a number expressed to a given degree of accuracy, using the knowledge, skills and understanding attained at lower levels in a wider range of contexts.

Algebra: calculating growth and decay rates and displaying them graphically, expressing general laws in symbolic form, using rules of indices for negative and fractional values, interpreting and using m and c in $y = mx+c$, solving equations using graphical methods.

Measures: calculating lengths of circular arcs and areas of shapes including circular arcs, calculating surface area of cylinders and volumes of cones and spheres.

Shape and space: calculating distances and angles in solids using plane sections and trigonometric ratios, understanding the conditions for congruent triangles, finding sine, cosine and tangent of angles of any size, using the relationship between surface areas of similar figures and for volumes of similar 3–D solids, understanding and using the laws of addition and subtraction of vectors.

Handling data: using sampling to investigate a "population" and recognising the reliability of different sizes of samples, constructing and interpreting a histogram with understanding of the connection between area and frequency, presenting a set of complex data in a simplified form using a variety of diagrams and graphs and computer statistical packages, producing a tree–diagram to illustrate the combined probability of several events which are not independent.

LEVEL 10

Using and applying mathematics: designing, planning and carrying through a mathematical task to a successful conclusion, presenting alternative solutions and justifying selected route, giving definitions which are sufficient or minimal, using symbolisation with confidence, constructing a proof including proof by contradiction.

Number: calculate the upper and lower bounds in the addition, subtraction, multiplication and division of numbers expressed to a given degree of accuracy,

using the knowledge, skills and understanding attained at lower levels in a wider range of contexts.

Algebra: using a calculator or computer to investigate whether a sequence given iteratively converges or diverges, manipulating a range of algebraic expressions in a variety of contexts, constructing tangents to graphs to determine the gradient, finding the approximate area between a curve and the horizontal axis between two limits, and interpreting the result, sketching the graph of functions derived from other functions.

Measures: determining the possible effects of error on calculations involving measurements.

Shape and space: knowing and using angle and tangent properties of circles, sketching the graphs of sine, cosine and tangent functions for all angles, generating trigonometric functions using a calculator or computer and interpreting them, using sine and cosine rules to solve problems including simple cases in 3–D, understanding how transformations are related by combinations and inverses, using matrices to define transformations in 2–D.

Handling data: describing the range of a variable using different measures of dispersion, calculating standard deviation of a set of data, interpreting various types of diagrams such as those used in analysis of critical path and linear programming, considering different shapes of histograms representing distributions with special reference to mean and dispersion including the normal distribution, understanding the probability for any two events happening.

Post 16 education

England has not a strong tradition of supplying technical and vocational education. Those institutions which provided it have not been well esteemed. Perhaps more importantly the provision of strong technical 'tracks' for pupils below the top 15% of the ability range has been lacking. Various bodies have provided qualifications in technical and business subjects, but these have been mainly acquired outside the school system within colleges of further and higher education. Within schools the major 16–18 qualification is A–level taken at 18+. Now, in an attempt to broaden post–16 education, for it is usual to take only 3 or 4 subjects at A–level standard (two, one, or none of which might be mathematics), a 'half' A–level, or AS, has been introduced.

It is A–level mathematics which we shall attempt to describe below. First, it must be noted that school examining in England was traditionally carried out by university controlled 'boards' – first from Oxford and Cambridge, later from other universities or groups of universities. Each offered a variety of syllabuses in 'Mathematics', 'Further Mathematics', 'Pure Mathematics', 'Applied Mathematics', 'Pure Mathematics with Statistics',... In the mid–1970s the number of different syllabuses offered rose to almost fifty.

So as to bring some degree of uniformity to the system, it was agreed that all 'basic' A–level mathematics courses should include a 'common core'. We begin by summarising that core.

Algebraic operations on polynomials and rational functions. Factors of polynomials. The factor theorem. Partial fractions (linear, repeated linear, simple quadratic). Positive and negative rational indices. The general quadratic in one variable: solution, completing the square, graph sketching, max and min. APs and GPs; sum to infinity of GP. Binomial expansion for positive integer exponent and for rational exponent with $-1 < x < 1$. Manipulation of simple algebraic inequalities. The modulus function.

Plane cartesian coordinates: an algebraic relation and its graph, line, simple form of equation for ellipse (no geometrical properties of conics). Effect of simple transformations on a graph. The relation of the equation of a graph to its symmetries. Expression of the coordinates (or position vector) of a point on a curve in terms of a parameter.

The six trigonometric functions for any angle; periodicity and symmetry. Sine and cosine formulae. Angles between line and plane, two planes, two skew lines (simple cases). Circular (radian) measure; length and area formulae.
Sin (A + B), sin (A – B) and for cosine and tangent, sin A + sin B etc. Knowledge of simple identities.
$a \cos \theta + b \sin \theta$. General solution of simple trigonometric equations; graphical interpretation. Approximations of sin x, tan x, cos x, for small x.

Vectors in two or three dimensions; algebraic operations of addition and multiplication by scalars, and their geometrical significance; the scalar product and its use in calculating angle between lines; position vectors; $\mathbf{r} = \mathbf{a} + t\mathbf{b}$.

Functions: inverse, composition, graphical relation with inverse. Exponential and logarithmic functions and simple properties. Limit notion. Derivative as limit. Gradient of a tangent as a limit. Differentiation of x^n, sin x, cos x, tan x, inverse trigonometric functions, e^x, a^x, ln x. Differentiation of sums, products and quotients, and of simple functions defined parametrically or implicitly. Applications of differentiation to gradients, tangents and normals, maxima and minima, curve sketching, rates of change, small increments and approximations. Integration as inverse of differentiation. Integration of standard functions (including use of inverse trig functions). Integration by substitution and by parts. Definite integrals with fixed limits. Integration and areas. Volumes of revolution.

Material not included in the common core, but likely to be found in an A–level syllabus includes:

Permutations and combinations. Complex numbers: basic algebra, Argand diagram, cartesian and polar representation. Numerical integration: trapezium rule and, possibly, Simpson's.

Other material which is commonly included, but possibly as an option to Statistics and Mechanics, includes:

Polar coordinates. Complex numbers: De Moivre for integral exponent, exponential form, simple applications. Matrix algebra and geometry.

Distance and angle properties, equations of lines and circles, and parametric equations for some conics.

Location of roots of an equation by graphical and simple numerical means, Newton–Raphson (first notions of considerations of convergence). Maclaurin's series with conditions for convergence of some standard series.

First order differential equations: separation of variables, use of simple substitutions. Second order homogeneous linear equations with constant coefficients.

Vectors in three dimensions. Two forms of scalar product, applications, vector equation of plane. Cartesian equations of lines and planes. Problems of lengths of projections, angles, perpendiculars.

A candidate for A–level may well have to take one or two options in addition to the common core, ie additional Pure Mathematics, Applied Mathematics, or Statistics. Possibly, work in all three areas may be expected.

A typical Applied Mathematics option is the following:

Forces treated as vectors, composition and resolution. Triangle and polygon of forces. Equilibrium. Friction. Moments and couples.

Kinematics of a particle moving in a straight line leading to first order DEs with separable variables. Relative motion.

Newton's Laws.

The motion of connected particles, single pulleys. Elastic strings and springs, Hooke's law.

Kinetic and potential energy, work, power. Conservation of energy.

Momentum and impulse, conservation of momentum for particles moving in a straight line.

Motion of a projectile. Uniform circular motion.

It will be seen that this option is drawn from particle mechanics. There are increasing attempts to introduce other applications of mathematics into the 16–19 curriculum, eg decision mathematics (simple graph theory and associated algorithms), electric circuit theory, information and coding theory. These, however, have not yet had much effect. In recent years less emphasis has been placed on the teaching of Newtonian mechanics. Certainly, since the 1960s much more emphasis has been placed on the teaching of statistics. (This can be studied as an free-standing A–level. However, this is often taken by those who are not studying mathematics at an advanced level. As a result, the mathematical demands it makes are kept low and do not include the differential calculus.) A typical statistics and probability option, offered as an alternative to the particle mechanics course described above is:

Theoretical and empirical interpretations of probability; basic probability laws, mutually exclusive events, conditional probability, independent events. (Not Bayes' theorem.)

Probability distributions for discrete random variables: uniform, geometric, binomial and Poisson distributions; their means and variances (no proofs). Poisson as approximation to the binomial (no proof).

Probability distributions for continuous random variables; probability density function; expectation, variance; cumulative distribution function; uniform and normal distributions; use of tables; normal as approximation to the binomial (no proof).

Ideas of sampling methods and distributions; approximate normality of distribution of sample mean (central limit – no proof). Estimation of population parameters from a sample; unbiasedness; confidence limits for population proportion and for the mean of large samples.

Hypothesis testing; null and alternative hypotheses; one– and two–tailed tests; tests of significance of a sample mean from a sample population (not t–test).

The number of A–level syllabuses available is very large indeed. What they include in addition to the common core varies correspondingly. It is impracticable to attempt to describe all the mathematics to be found in them. It would also be of interest only for historians. Official steps are already being taken drastically to reduce the number of syllabuses on offer. New regulations will come into effect from 1994. The example above will suffice to illustrate typical content coverage.

The A–level mathematics examination is taken by fewer than 7 percent of the age cohort. Moreover, since 1984 the proportion of the cohort entering the examination has fallen. (Because of the demographic dip, numbers fell by over 20% between 1984 and 1990.) In 1989 a new examination, AS, equivalent to half an A–level was instituted. Originally this course was supposed to be offered in two forms: contrasting and complementary. The contrasting AS was intended for the Arts student who did not necessarily wish to spend time acquiring the techniques of the differential calculus; the complementary AS for the scientist or engineer who, for some reason or other, did not enter for A–level. The latter AS has, therefore, come to resemble the common core for A–level, and is even taken in some schools to be a stepping–stone to A–level to be attempted at 17+ (end of Grade 11).

A typical time allocation for A–level mathematics is about five hours per week. About one quarter of those taking A–level Mathematics study for a second mathematics A–level, Further Mathematics. (The timetabled hours for this are normally less than for "single–subject" mathematics.)

Again, there are many alternative syllabuses for Further Mathematics. Normally there will be a choice of content offered within any one syllabus. To give some idea of the mathematical coverage and depth expected we briefly summarise one such course.

A knowledge of the corresponding A-level syllabus (including all its Pure Mathematics) will normally be assumed. Additional Pure topics which are "more or less" compulsory are:

Polynomial functions and equations (relations between coefficients and symmetric functions of roots). Simple rational algebraic functions and their graphs. Summation of finite series. Mathematical induction.

The six hyperbolic functions and their inverses, related integrals. Further differentiation and integration; reduction formulae, finding second derivatives in parametric and implicit cases. Application of integration to mean values, centroids, lengths of curves and areas of surfaces of revolution.

Solution of first order DEs using integrating factor. Second order inhomogeneous linear DEs with constant coefficients. Solution of DEs using substitutions.

Proof of De Moivre for positive integral exponent; applications to, eg, powers of sin A and cos A. Loci in the Argand plane and simple transformations.

Candidates would then be expected to study at least one of:

Algebraic structure Relations, equivalence, equivalence classes. Binary operations; identity and inverse elements. Properties and examples of groups (subgroups, order of element, Lagrange (no proof)). Isomorphisms between groups.

Matrices and linear spaces Linear space, subspaces (only over the reals). Linear dependence and independence. Row space and column space of a matrix; basis of subspace. Rank and dimension. Matrices as linear transformations. Eigenvalues and eigenvectors (2×2 and 3×3).

Vectors Ratio theorem and applications; lines and planes. Vector product (determinant form). Applications of scalar and vector products.

In addition to this Pure Mathematics, students will take an extra paper in either:

Mechanics Rigid bodies. Systems of forces in three dimensions. Moments and vector products. Equivalent systems of forces. Necessary and sufficient conditions for equilibrium of a system. Centre of mass. Moments of inertia. Relative velocity. Radial and tangential acceleration in circular motion. Motion in a vertical circle. Simple harmonic motion: small oscillations, simple pendulum. Impulse and momentum. Coefficient of restitution. Oblique impact of smooth spheres and of sphere with plane. Motion of rigid body about fixed axis; kinetic energy, equation of angular motion; the compound pendulum.

or

Statistics Geometric, hypergeometric, negative exponential and Cauchy distributions. Probability generating functions. Bivariate distributions; marginal and conditional distributions; covariance, independence. The use (but not the mathematical theory) of the t and chi-squared tests. Bivariate samples; scatter diagrams; linear correlation and regression coefficients, regression lines and least squares. Confidence limits for regression coefficient. Non-parametric tests of significance: sign test, Wilcoxson rank test, Spearman's and Kendall's rank correlation coefficients.

or

Numerical analysis (together with some statistics and/or mechanics) Errors, absolute and relative. Approximations using partial derivatives but with no theory of partial differentiation. Loss of significant figures in calculations. Approximations to functions by polynomials. Estimation of errors in such approximations. Solution of equations by interval bisection, iterative procedures, computation of successive corrections (some consideration of convergence expected). Linear systems of equations, Gaussian elimination. Concept of ill-conditioned set of equations. Numerical integration; extension of trapezium rule, Romberg integration; extension of Simpson's rule. Bounds for errors. Use of Lagrangian interpolating polynomial. Step by step solution of DEs. Taylor series method. Predictor-corrector approach. Simple curve fitting using least squares. Functions of one variable tabulated at equal intervals. Definitions of standard operators and their relationships. Use of these in simple cases.

ABOUT THE MATHEMATICAL ASSOCIATION

The Mathematical Association is for you if you teach mathematics at any age or stage from 4 years onwards. You do not need to be a high-powered mathematician to belong to the Association. One of its strengths is that it brings together primary, secondary and university teachers, industrialists and advisers. Membership is available to individuals, primary schools and institutions.

Benefits of membership

Journals and Periodicals

According to the subscription paid members receive one or more of the following journals:

(i) *The Mathematical Gazette* is published four times a year. It offers articles on current issues in mathematical teaching at all levels of secondary school, college and university. It includes full book reviews.

(ii) *Mathematics in School* is published five times a year covering the teaching of the 7–16 age range. It is a lively, brightly coloured magazine, closely related to the classroom.

(iii) *Prism Packs* are published three times a year and are aimed at teachers of primary pupils, students in training and all those with an interest in primary mathematics education.

(iv) *Mathematics Round the Country* is of particular interest to primary teachers and is obtainable directly from the Association or, at a reduced rate for quantity, through your local education authority.

(v) *Struggle,* published jointly with the National Association for Remedial Education, three times a year, is concerned with the teaching of low attainers.

Reports

Members receive, at no extra charge, a copy of new reports allocated to their membership category which have been produced by the Teaching Committee.

Journals for Pupils

(i) *Mathematical Pie* is published termly and is aimed at lower secondary pupils. It contains many interesting and useful articles, games and puzzles.

(ii) *Plus* is also published termly and is for upper school pupils. Both can be purchased in bulk from the Association for resale to your pupils.

Newsletter

News and information about the Association's activities, branches and matters of interest nationally and internationally is sent to members in the MA Newsletter published three times a year.

Reduced Prices

The comprehensive range of publications and reports issued by the Association is offered at discounted prices to members.

General

Members may attend the annual conference and any of the seminars organised by the Association, may borrow books from the library housed at Leicester University and may send their problems to be solved by the Problem Bureau. Members may join their local branch and meet other members in their locality. The MA awards diplomas and certificates to teachers who have followed accredited courses at centres around the country.

Members are encouraged to become actively involved in the MA by writing for the journals, becoming members of the various committees (national and local) and by offering their services to the Diploma Board.

Since 1871 the Mathematical Association has provided a forum for all those interested in mathematics and in improving the teaching of mathematics. It is run, voluntarily, by teachers, lecturers and other mathematicians. There is a small permanent staff at the Headquarters in Leicester, from where the Association continues to expand its work of improving the teaching of mathematics.

For full details of services and membership contact:
The Mathematical Association, 259 London Road, Leicester, LE2 3BE (0533) 703877